PU

AND JUDY

ARNOLD BENNETT

Edited and with an Introduction
by John Shapcott
University of Keele

Foreword by Margaret Drabble

CHURNET VALLEY BOOKS
6 Stanley Street, Leek, Staffordshire ST13 5HG 01538 399033

ISBN 9781904546832

To Linda
with love

The cover is a painting by Sally Richardson

One of a series of Arnold Bennett titles, in both a paperback and a limited and numbered hardback edition:

HELEN WITH THE HIGH HAND
LEONORA
THE REGENT
THE PRICE OF LOVE
A MAN FROM THE NORTH
THE OLD WIVES' TALE
THE PRETTY LADY
THE CARD
ARNOLD BENNETT'S UNCOLLECTED SHORT STORIES
LORD DOVER & OTHER LOST STORIES

CONTENTS

PUNCH AND JUDY

FOREWORD

Arnold Bennett's contributions to the history of cinema have been overlooked and undervalued, according to John Shapcott's persuasive and informative Introduction to the scenario of *Punch and Judy*, which is published here and made available to the reading public for the first time. He makes a strong case for Bennett's grasp of cinematic narrative, and for the importance of the new medium of film in the creative spirit of the age. In his Introduction to Bennett's 1914 novel, *The Price of Love*, Shapcott provided us with a brilliantly revealing account of the cultural and social impact of the 'crystal dream' of the new picture palaces and silent movies, and he follows through here with a detailed analysis of Bennett's views on film, on his engagement with the industry, his dislike of the talkies, and his sometimes surprising assessments of well-known films of the day. He also records Bennett's reactions to Charlie Chaplin, Alfred Hitchcock, Gloria Swanson, Ronald Colman and other stars; the confrontation with the legendary Hitchcock is particularly intriguing. And we are given a carefully researched literary context for Flitfoot, the monstrous financier anti-hero of this dark script, citing Theodore Dreiser, whom Bennett greatly admired, and describing one of Dreiser's originals, Charles Tyson Yerkes, the American entrepreneur who became a father of the London underground system.

E. A. Dupont's 1929 film of Bennett's original screenplay *Piccadilly* has recently been digitally restored, and the opportunity to see it on screen in London's Chinatown convinced me that Shapcott was right to suggest that I and earlier critics and biographers had unfairly neglected this aspect of his work. It is of considerable artistic and great sociological interest. Shapcott has now given us a chance to consider his treatment of *Punch and Judy*, a tale of financial ruthlessness that is even more topical today than when it was written. Bennett, who prided himself on being a man of the world, canny about money, explores in this story the world of take-over bids and shady share dealing, and creates new twentieth-century types such as Flitfoot's cigar-smoking personal assistant, Miss Sligo. This is a fascinating recovery of a lost moment of the early years of film history, painstakingly reassembled and documented by one of Bennett's most scholarly advocates. It also shows us the Arnold Bennett who was ever ready to take on the new, the Modernist Bennett who enjoyed the challenge of the future.

Margaret Drabble 2011

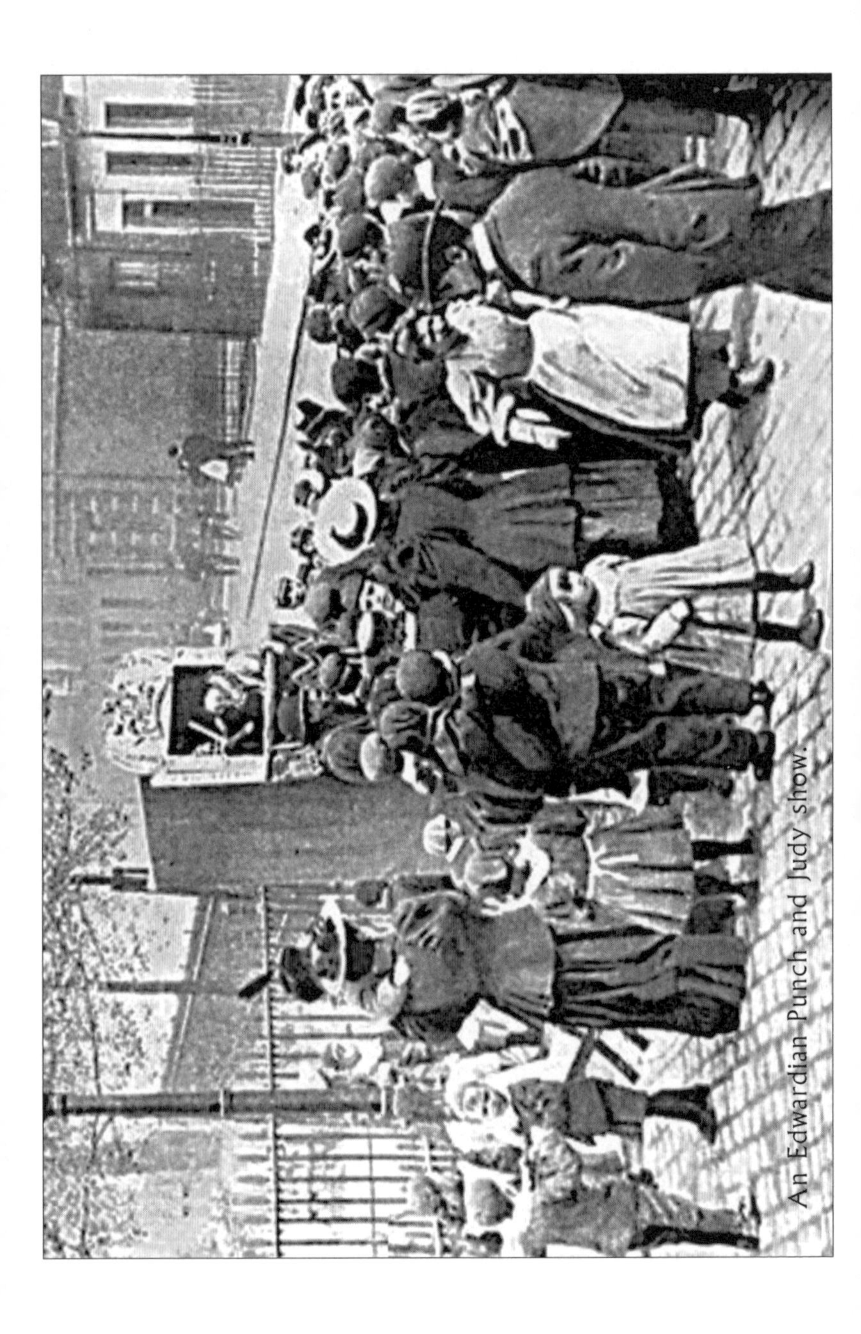

An Edwardian Punch and Judy show.

INTRODUCTION
ARNOLD BENNETT AND SILENT CINEMA

There is a convincing case to be made for regarding Arnold Bennett as the most important professionally engaged early twentieth-century writer dealing with the world of cinema and film. From the publication of the *The Regent* in 1913, with one of the earliest references to film in the English novel, in a short passage on the cinematograph's invasion of the music-hall,[1] to the release of the 1929 E. A. Dupont's film *Piccadilly* based on Bennett's original script, Bennett remained critically aware of the importance of film as an artistic and commercial medium. His involvement with the medium spans the most important period of the development, and rapid demise, of silent film as a narrative art form. In addition to his own original screenplays, cinema articles and essays, journal entries on films seen and stars met, and a ground-breaking extensive reference to cinemas and their programmes in his 1914 novel *The Price of Love*, Bennett was also the beneficiary of film producers' interest in his literary work. Silent film adaptations of his novels included *The Great Adventure* (1916, 1921), *Sacred and Profane Love* (1921), *The Old Wives' Tale* (1921), *The Card* (1922) and *The City of Pleasure* (1929), all of which had world-wide distribution. Bennett's published journals and letters give no indication of him taking any other than a financial interest in these film adaptations - he estimated his film earnings up to 1923 at £6,400 - not even commenting on the quality of the inter-titles, a subject on which he held strongly expressed views.

Bennett's earliest direct involvement with the film

1. For a brief discussion on the importance of this early literary cinematograph reference see the 'Introduction' to *The Regent,* p.xiii (Churnet Valley Books).

industry came in 1920 when he wrote a scenario, *The Wedding Dress*, at the request of film producer Jesse Lasky. This was never produced and the experience left Bennett feeling sufficiently frustrated to voice his discontent in his essay 'In the Film World' (*The Savour of Life*, 1928). It was not until October 1926 that Bennett re-engaged with film-work when he agreed with Wardour Films to write the inter-titles for the English release of the German film *Faust*, directed by F.W. Murnau.[2] In characteristically forthright fashion Bennett wrote to his literary agent, Eric Pinker, 'The film is not as good as they think it is, but I can make it better' (*Letters Vol.I*, p.357). Bennett's major contribution to silent film history, however, came late in life when, on 30 January 1929, *Piccadilly* received its first, private, showing at the Carlton Theatre in London's Haymarket, before going on general release. James Hepburn notes that 'Bennett wrote two scripts [for *Piccadilly*], working all day on 14 April 1928 to produce the first one. He then wrote the second, and from it or from them both composed a 17,000-word film story in two weeks, finishing on 24 May' (*Critical Heritage*, p.109). The story was serialised in *Film Weekly* and published in book form, with stills from the film, in March 1929 by The Readers Library Publishing Company. The 'Editor's Note' that prefaces the book goes to some lengths to establish Bennett's literary credentials before extending them to comment on his role as a screen writer. The argument on originality and self-containment is equally

2. Iris Barry, influential film critic and founder member of the Film Society in 1925, concluded her review of *Faust* by remarking: 'It was with infinite glee that I observed a grammatical slip in one of the English sub-titles which have been written by Mr. Arnold Bennett' (The Spectator, 8 January 1927, page 39). *The Daily Express* cinema correspondent, however, chose to begin rather than end his review by praising Bennett's titles before proceeding to criticise a 'dismal "Faust"': 'Germany's most elaborate screen-nightmare is "Faust", which Mr. C. B. Cochran presented at the Albert Hall last evening, for a short run, with music specially provided by Sir Landon Ronald, and sub-titles written by Mr. Arnold Bennett, who has done his work extremely well' (*Daily Express,* 3 January 1927).

A digitally restored German negative of the film was released on DVD in 2006 in the *Masters of Cinema* series but with newly written inter-titles.

applicable to the story of *Punch and Judy*:

> Now Mr. Bennett is performing a new part, as the writer of the story for a modern super-film.... We have great pleasure in publishing ....the author's original story for the film. It will be agreed this is a most interesting publication. And the tale as written here is a complete work of art in itself....The characters in the book ....live and move in these pages without any translation to the screen being necessary. And their story is as real and dramatic in Mr. Bennett's polished and vivid writing as it could be in any other medium except life itself.
>
> (*Piccadilly*, p.9)

Ever the perfectionist, with unlimited self-belief, Bennett wrote to Frederick Wicken, Pinker's managing clerk, that the 'end of the film is not really ended at all.... I could have obtained a much better film if I had lived at Elstree during the shooting, but this of course is impossible' (*Letters*, *Vol.III*, p.389). But Bennett was pleased with positive reviews from the majority of critics and by its box-office success. It is particularly interesting in the light of Bennett's comment above that he wrote very specific directions for the beginning and ending of *Punch and Judy* that, as I hope to show, provide evidence of a keen sense of cinematic narrative. Given the overall artistic and commercial success of the film and the pleasure Bennett derived from mixing in the company of film-stars, however, it is not surprising to find Bennett immersing himself in further film writing and anticipating success with another scenario, *Punch and Judy*, commissioned by J.C.A. Thorpe, manager of Wardour Films, in Autumn 1928.

Bennett's published *Journal* provides several snapshots of the film scenario's rapid progress between late September to mid-December 1928:

'We left Victoria for Annecy at 2 p.m. In the French train Dorothy [Cheston Bennett] and I discussed my *Punch and Judy* film at some length' (4 September).

'I then reflected for one hour on my film and I got a real notion or two' (6 September).

'I walked out in the morning – Chelsea Embankment and got a few ideas for completing a scene of *Punch and Judy*, and finished the scene before lunch' (1 November).

'Dr. Griffin called to see me, so that I could get from him medical details for *Punch and Judy*' (4 November).

'Walked around Shaftesbury Avenue, etc. to Reform Club to get ideas for *Punch and Judy*. I got some, and I got more at the Club between 12.30 and 1. I did a little writing of the film between 5 and 6.30' (3 December).

'.... hated to start work, did start, and in 90 minutes had written a chapter of *Punch and Judy*' (10 December).

Bennett's handwritten alterations and corrections to Winifred Nerney's[3] typescript for Parts I and III, dated 17 December 1928, includes his signature word count, although his reckoning of 37,000 words for the complete manuscript does, in fact, under-record the total by some 3,700 words. In any event, *Punch and Judy* is a considerably more substantial work than the 18,000 word published book of *Piccadilly.*

Parts I and III are particularly interesting in a cinema context for the evidence they provide of Bennett's very real understanding of the mechanics of film making of the time. His approach mirrors Eisenstein's presupposition of overt narration, in which, as David Bordwell summarises it, there is 'an invisible master of ceremonies who has staged this action, chosen these camera positions, and edited the images in just

3. Winifred Nerney was Bennett's devoted secretary from 1912 onwards.

this way' so that there is 'a continual awareness of the director's shaping hand' (*Narration*, p.15). In a handwritten 'Preliminary note' to the story Bennett writes that the 'scenario, however, is much longer [than that of *Piccadilly*], because the descriptions, and particularly the dialogue, are much more detailed, so as to give every assistance to the Director about environment, circumstances, and motives'. He clearly envisages a virtuoso work with a degree of innovative camera positions as in, for example, his suggestion for the framing of a point-of-view shot from inside the Punch and Judy booth. Another example of Bennett's reluctance to cede interpretation to the director occurs in the prefatory remarks to Chapter XVII where he introduces the idea of cross-cutting two distinct lines of narration to give the impression of events occurring simultaneously and at the same time using the technique to highlight the differing fortunes of the two main financially motivated characters, Flitfoot and Sir Joshua Massingham. In addition to introducing the idea of cross-cutting as a stylistic vehicle for manipulating time sequences, Bennett is also keen to introduce a sophisticated level of symbolism, inspired perhaps by his cinema viewing of Russian symbolist film and German expressionist drama: 'Just as the movements of Punch the puppet are actuated by cords or other devices, so if the Director finds it advisable might the movements of Flitfoot seem sometimes (in crisis) to be actuated by mysterious cords, pulling at his hands etc.' Despite Bennett's seeming deferral to the director's judgement, he nevertheless proceeds to insert a number of references to 'invisible cords' appearing to the viewer at crucially dramatic moments. These first appear in Chapter V when Flitfoot is drawn to take advantage of being left alone to steal a pill-box containing the pill with which he intends to poison the dog, Toby. They continue to appear at regular intervals until the final scene where they 'positively dragged' Flitfoot towards his nemesis on the site which should have represented his greatest financial triumph.

There is an element of showy craftsmanship on display in Bennett's narrative interventions to suggest edited images, but they are also evidence of his ability to focus on the pictorial production values of drama whilst writing a coherent narrative. These considerations are important in the context of British film production in the late 1920s when, for example, 'the *Daily Sketch* laments the failure of British authors, "conservative and contemptuous of modern developments", to write for the cinema' (Gledhill, p.52).

Bennett's choice of the traditional Punch and Judy story and its characters as the central symbolic controlling motif of the film is far from fortuitous. He is on record as contending that 'Punch-and-Judy is theatre, and perhaps the best. For myself I would sooner watch Punch-and-Judy for a quarter of an hour for twopence than a West End drawing-room comedy for two hours and a half for twelve shillings' (*Evening Standard*, 6 March 1930, p.7). Cost apart, he goes on in the same article to argue that it 'has other advantages' that are relevant for the would-be screenwriter: 'Clear plots. Swift action. Satisfactory murders. Farce as broad as the Mall. Total absence of love-scenes' (ibid).

In adapting the traditional Punch and Judy format for a contemporary screenplay Bennett also adopts a conceit from William Thackeray's *Vanity Fair* (1847) with its 'Before the Curtain' preface to the novel proper – 'As the Manager of the Performance sits before the curtain on the boards, and looks into the Fair, a feeling of profound melancholy comes over him in his survey of the bustling place' (p.1) and his short concluding paragraph reducing the preceding panoramic human drama to a puppet play. Bennett greatly admired Thackeray, recommending his novels in his journalistic pieces,[4] and there can be little doubt that he consciously modelled Parts I and III of his film scenario on Thackeray's puppet prologue and epilogue. Whilst the prefatory narrative similarities are obvious and not particularly innovative on Bennett's part, his inter-media re-interpretation of Thackeray's epilogue is a masterly transfer from one artistic medium to another and represents an act of homage to a revered canonical literary ancestor. Thackeray concludes: 'Ah! *Vanitas Vanitatum!* Which of us is happy in this world? Which of us has his desire? or, having it, is satisfied?–Come children, let us shut up the box and the puppets, for our play is played out' (p.878). This and his parting self-penned illustration of the puppets' return to their box – reproduced here – is uncannily echoed in Bennett's epilogue.

4. Between March 1898 and July 1927 Bennett published 14 periodical articles about Thackeray. The first of these appeared in *Hearth and Home* written under the pen name of Sarah Volatile and the last, looking at Thackeray's place amongst the 'Great Victorian Novelists' in his influential *Evening Standard* column. Bennett also includes Thackeray's *Vanity Fair, Henry Esmund* and *Barry Lyndon* as essential constituents of an English library in his *Literary Taste. How To Form It* (1909).

Both the writers reduce their characters to puppets under the control of the puppet master/narrator and in the process create different levels of reality and complexity.

Where for Thackeray, however, 'our play is played out' with this final single static image, Bennett is able to call upon the potential of cinematic technique to fill the screen with multiple images of 'hundreds of Punch and Judy shows' and modernity's proliferation of images. Contemporary directors such as the young Alfred Hitchcock had experimented with multiple images in, for example, *Champagne* (1928) but Bennett's innovative vision only achieves full expression twenty years later in Orson Welles's use of multiple mirrors in *The Lady of Shanghai* (1948).

Bennett's ability and willingness to bring his literary knowledge to the medium of film without sacrificing any of the subtleties that evade the majority of his contemporary British film writers make him a unique figure. Rachel Low, in her magisterial *The History of British Film 1918-1929*, writes that the 'low opinion of the script was a great weakness in the British industry [which] underrated the importance of the story itself and seemed to justify ....turning everything into the same formula stuff' (p.240). An added problem was that it 'was widely assumed that stories must come from outside the industry. The publicity values of famous books was realized, but the main reason for borrowing so heavily from them was that hardly anybody wrote directly for the screen' (ibid, p.241).

Bennett was sympathetic to the difficulties involved in film-making and was, indeed, often very appreciative of both the aesthetic and the technical achievements of the medium. Writing, for example, about E.A. Dupont's *Vaudeville* (made in 1926 and originally titled *Variety*) in the film magazine

Close Up[5] Bennett praises the 'photography [which] was beautiful. By which I mean that the pictorial composition, both statically and dynamically was beautiful. The eye was again and again charmed by the beautiful pictures made out of men and women and out of common interiors. To achieve this was a feat' ('The Film "Story"', reprinted in *Sight and Sound*, p.165 and in Appendix I of this volume). At the same time, he laments that too many fine compositional results are undermined because 'the story told by the lovely picture was contemptible. It had no intelligible basic idea, nor any convincingness, nor any characterisation, nor any beauty. The plot was involved, obscure, and slow in movement. And the invention of illustrative incident was puerile. Indeed the story was merely foolish' (ibid, p.165). For Bennett the problem is that 'the leaders of the cinema have not yet grasped the fundamental truth that the most important part of any creative film is the story itself, and that all other parts of the enterprise are merely parts of an effort to tell the story' (ibid, p.165). The remedy for these ills appeared obvious and Bennett's diagnosis makes fascinating, if contradictory, reading in the light of his own imminent original screenplay for Dupont's *Piccadilly*, and the subsequent protracted negotiations over his carefully constructed *Punch and Judy* screenplay:

> If and when a producer acquires the true sense of proportion which alone will enable him to perceive the

5. *Close Up*, edited by Kenneth Macpherson, the novelist Bryher and the poet H.D., was published between 1927 and 1933. One of its most regular and influential contributors was Dorothy Richardson, whose September 1927 article 'Captions' (reprinted in *Close Up 1927-1933. Cinema and Modernism,* pp.164-165) is particularly relevant given Bennett's determination not to allow *Punch and Judy* to be made as a talkie. The edited selection of *Close Up* entries unfortunately omits Bennett's contribution with the result of skewing its representation towards modernist writers and suggesting a concomitant lack of serious analytical interest from realist writers. Laura Marcus's otherwise excellent *The Tenth Muse. Writing about Cinema in the Modernist Period* (2007) similarly overlooks Bennett's cinema work, in part, perhaps understandably, because much of it remains to be published. This side-lining of Bennett means that, for example, we lack a comprehensive and productive analysis of late 1920s British films' cultural values that would benefit from a comparative study of Kenneth Macpherson's silent *Borderline* (1930) and Bennett/Dupont's *Piccadilly* (1929).

> relative importance of the different parts of his job, he must, unless he has himself the gift of creating character and contriving event, find somebody who has that gift – in terms of the screen. Useless for him to go to established and therefore middle-aged masters of literary narration. To all these distinguished artists the screen is still a novelty. The film-medium does not come naturally to them because they were not familiar with it in their formative years – the only years that count in the making of an artist. The producer must discover young men who went to the cinema as children, who cannot remember the time when there was no cinema, and who will take to the screen as a duck takes to water. The older men who accept an invitation to the screen are bound to resemble ducks endeavouring to fly. They may fly, but their flight will be laborious, maladroit and pathetic.
>
> ('The Film "Story"', p.166)

Bennett's article appeared during a decisive period of change for the British film industry and it is intriguing that it should have been published in an early edition of *Close Up*, which advertised itself as 'an English review ....the first to approach films from the angle of art, experiment, and possibility' (from the cover wrapper, Vol.I, no.4, October 1927). All three of these qualities are central to Bennett's screenwriting analysis and practice and had he been afforded the opportunity to write for *Close Up* again in the light of his late but highly successful entry into film, then it seems likely that he would have revised his opinion of the inevitability of the older generation doomed to a 'laborious, maladroit and pathetic' experience. He would also have needed to consider his friend H. G. Wells's wide-sweeping epic scenario, *The King Who Was a King. The Book of a Film* (1929), exploring the possibilities of bringing the theme 'World Peace' to the screen and outlining a programme for cinema as an art form in a 35 page introductory chapter, 'The Development of the Film'.[6]

Bennett's mature appreciation of the central elements of silent film technique unfortunately coincided with the birth of sound film and its rapidly developing public popularity. He could never bring himself to acknowledge the possibilities of sound film, and, at a time when he was acrimoniously involved in discussions about making *Punch and Judy* as a talkie, his 1929 *Journal* entries offer evidence of an implacable hostility to the coming of sound:

> *London, May 14th* [1929]
> Invited to a midnight special performance of 'Bull-dog Drummond' (the film) at the Tivoli, with Ronald Colman as Drummond .... The film was stated to be the first talkie ever done. And perhaps it was .... [but very] curious, disconcerting, is the appearance of a slim, elegant, fragile, spiritual-faced woman, followed by a terrific booming noise – the lady's voice!
> (*Journal 1929*, p.37)

> *London, September* [1929]
> I went by invitation to the world première of an English written and English directed talking film, in which Gloria Swanson was the star.... My opinion of Gloria Swanson's gifts as an actress in silent films is very high indeed.... The talking film began.... Crude, tawdry, grossly sentimental, encumbered with stretches of acutely tedious and undramatic dialogue, and rendered ugly by the sound of the human voice which mars all talking films, it crawled along from unforeseen crisis to crisis in the most exasperating manner.... I left the theatre saddened by this spectacle of the waste of a first-rate artist. (*Journal 1929*, pp.123-126)

6. Wells's place in the history of British cinema is explored in detail in Keith Williams's *H.G. Wells. Modernity and the Movies* (2007).

In fairness to Bennett it should be noted that he was far from alone in his dislike of sound films. In 1928, for example, the influential film critic Ernest Betts, a contributor to *Close Up*, published *Heraclitus, or the Future of Films*, a book exploring film as an art form, in which he argued that 'films should be seen and not heard .... There is something monstrous about a speaking film.... The two effects, marching out of step, carry the mind and senses different ways, and leave the spectator in conflict with himself.... The soul of the film - its eloquent and vital silence is destroyed' (quoted in *The Tenth Muse,* p.369). Both Dorothy Richardson and H.D. used *Close Up* to continue to press for the aesthetic privileging of silent films. Richardson wrote that sound was a crude mechanical intrusion into the medium that in destroying live musical accompaniment 'fragmented the continuous stream provided by film music in silent cinema and its unifying aesthetic' (Marcus, p.405). H.D. admitted the potential of sound but regretted that it came at the expense of 'that half-world of lights and music and blurred perception.... into which the being floats as a moth into summer darkness' *(Close Up 1927-1933*, p.306). More prosaically, but to the same point, the film theorist Paul Rotha, writing in 1930 when the sound film had triumphed, warned that '[i]mmediately a voice begins to speak in a cinema, the sound apparatus takes precedence over the camera, thereby doing violence to natural instincts' (*Film Till Now*, p.306).

It is against this critical background warning of a perceived aesthetic threat to the medium of film as pure art that Bennett's reluctance to see *Punch and Judy* made as a talkie should be understood. To date, Margaret Drabble's biography of Bennett remains the only study to have included any reference to *Punch and Judy* and Bennett's argument with Hitchcock, but her conclusion that '[f]ilm as an art form and film as a popular medium defeated him' (*Arnold Bennett*, p.329) was reached without the benefit of the digitally restored print of *Piccadilly* and the subsequent revisionist critical commentary, and without access to the film scenario for either *The Wedding Dress* or *Punch and Judy*. Bennett's published *Journal* also offered glimpses of his appreciation of silent film as an art form. He was, for example, a great admirer of Charlie Chaplin, finding 'a few fine moments' (*Journal*, p.1004) in his 1928 film *The Circus*. He was particularly enthusiastic about Emil Jannings's 1926 film *Vaudeville*: 'It is very fine, despite a simple and rather crude story. All the pictures make "designed pictures". I should say that the prisoners' exercise was inspired by Van Gogh. Even the empty interiors are like Cézanne. The close-ups are wonderful in design' (*Journal*, p.867). It should also be noted in defence of Bennett's knowledge and understanding of silent film that the Film Society[7] and Wardour Films thought him a suitably qualified person to call upon in November 1927 to arbitrate between their respective preferred versions of a German film about health-culture.

When Bennett and Hitchcock met in January 1929 to discuss filming *Punch and Judy*, Bennett came away under the impression that the young director had largely deferred to his judgement. (Bennett's account of this meeting, in *Journal 1929*, is reprinted in Appendix II of this volume.) His subsequent report of the meeting to Wicken sounds a confident note:

> I had a long interview with Thorpe and Hitchcock last night about the new film *Punch and Judy*. Hitchcock is to be the producer. He talked a good deal about wanting more 'colour' – a great film word – and had various

7. The Film Society was formed in London in 1925 by Ivor Montague and Hugh Miller, and administered by Iris Barry. Its brief was to show films not available on General Release but which it considered likely to appeal to a serious minority audience.

> absurd suggestions for changing the general environment of the film (which I have made chiefly financial). I argued with him for three hours, and defeated him on every point. Thorpe openly argued on my side and against his own man. Towards the end Hitchcock's principal phrase was 'I agree. I agree.' He finished by saying that he would prepare a few leading ideas for the actual scenario. Thorpe is certainly very pleased with the film, and I assume that he definitely intends to take it substantially as it is. Anyhow I shall alter it, if I alter it, only in small details.
>
> (*Letters Vol.I*, p. 388)

Just six weeks later, however, and Bennett is again writing to Wicken, but by now he is aware that he misread the situation and that Hitchcock has no intention of letting the writer have things all his own way:

> .... As I have previously told you, I think, Hitchcock's arguments made no impression upon me at all, and as the discussion proceeded Thorpe took more and more my side, until he definitely ranged himself on my side. There remained nothing to argue about. Hitchcock, when they left me, said that he would put his ideas for a scenario down on paper within the next ensuing few days. Since then about six weeks have elapsed and I have heard nothing at all from either Hitchcock or Thorpe. In no circumstances shall I accept any of the ideas which Hitchcock suggested and which I rejected with Thorpe's full sympathy. I finished the interview with the clear impression that the story was to be accepted as it stood. Thorpe of course did not actually say so. For one thing he is always very cautious, and for another he could not well give an acceptance in the presence of Hitchcock, after Hitchcock had elaborated his general notion that I should entirely change the

> milieu of the story and make all the characters characters in a circus.
>
> (*Letters Vol.I*, p.391)

Whilst it is understandable that Bennett objected to the idea of re-writing the scenario to a circus setting, at the same time he gave no indication of appreciating Hitchcock's rapidly growing reputation.[8] In the previous 17 months, Hitchcock had both written and directed *The Ring*, and directed successful adaptations of Eden Phillpotts's play *The Farmer's Wife*, Walter C. Mycroft's *Champagne* and Hall Caine's *The Manxman*. They all had screenplays by Eliot Stannard,[9] who had worked on all but one of Hitchcock's silent films. Stannard always allowed Hitchcock to take the major credit for the films on which they had collaborated, and Bennett's wish to control his own screenplay was a direct challenge to Hitchcock's assumed directorial autonomy, a threat that must have been taken into account when accounting for the acrimonious break-up of negotiations. As an additional irritant, questions of money were beginning to play a leading role alongside that of creative input, with Bennett demanding an immediate payment of £1,000 in early March. Differences quickly escalated when Hitchcock introduced the idea of filming *Punch and Judy* as a talkie. On 19 March Bennett was again writing to Wicken in combative mode: 'If I am to work further on *Punch and Judy* with a view to making it into a "talkie", I will not accept less than £2,000 extra.... It will be

8. 'In May of 1926, even before Hitchcock's [highly commercially and aesthetically successful] Gainsborough film *The Lodger* ....had been shown, B. I. P. had signed up this brilliant young director for £13,000 and were clearly pinning their hopes on him' (Low, *British Film, 1918-1929*, p. 177).

9. Eliot Stannard commands scant attention in studies of silent film and yet he was one of the most prolific and successful of screenwriters, responsible for over 300 scenarios at the time of Bennett's involvement with Hitchcock. His manual on *Writing Screen-Plays* (1920) emphasises the point that Bennett also made in his sometimes dismissive comments on silent films' lack of a coherent plot, that a 'successful film-play depends as much upon the soundness of its central theme as a stage play or novel' (quoted in Charles Barr, *English Hitchcock*, p.25).

more trouble to write *Punch and Judy* for a silent film and then turn it into a talkie film, and will involve more work than to have written it direct for a talkie' (*Letters Vol.I*, p.393). In the same letter Bennett is adamant that he will not permit filming with sound unless he is allowed complete control over writing the dialogue. By 2 May, however, Bennett is conceding defeat and writing that 'I shall have nothing to do with dialogue. B.I.P. [British International Pictures] are perfectly entitled to turn the picture into a "talkie".... but they are not entitled to ask me to have anything to do with the dialogue. I contracted to supply a story, which story I have supplied' (*Letters Vol.I*, p.395). Finally, by 12 July, the whole project appears dead, with Bennett realising that neither Hitchcock, nor his preferred alternative director E.A. Dupont, will make the film, writing that 'In any case I would *in no circumstances* agree to Hitchcock, as I am quite sure he would spoil the thing[10].... Anyhow there is no hurry. If nothing is done, then I have received £1,000 & the story remains mine' (*Letters Vol.I*, p.397). The story did remain his, and his alone, for although it is mentioned in biographies and bibliographies, it does not appear to have been seen or read by any of Bennett's critics, receiving no attention as either a story/novel in its own right or as an important document relating to the last years of British silent films. For over 80 years it has been a forgotten early casualty of the kinds of creative-control disputes which were to frustrate writers such as William Faulkner, Ernest Hemingway and F. Scott Fitzgerald in the Hollywood studios of the 1930s.

The story we are left with is one of the most amoral of all

10. The irony here is that in August 1929 Hitchcock released his sound version of his June silent film *Blackmail*, now regarded, in Bryony Dixon's 2011 survey, as 'one of, if not *the*, best British films of the late 1920s'. Dixon writes that Hitchcock 'managed to simultaneously produce a beautifully crafted silent film and a sound version, tackling the considerable technical obstacles of adding dialogue with such an imaginative and intelligent approach that it has become more famous for this aspect of its composition than for its quality as a film.' (*100 Silent Films*, p.36).

Bennett's texts, featuring a hero with absolutely no redeeming traits and surrounded by a supporting cast of characters who either connive with his chicanery, often to their own perceived financial advantage, or are ineffectual in preventing his grosser excesses. Flitfoot, Punch's filmic avatar, is the first and last major character to appear in the story and he remains throughout the central actor motivating the plot. Every narrative path leads either to him or away from him because he is literally and metaphorically plugged into the wires of the main plot development, centred on an attempt to monopolise control of London's electricity supply. Flitfoot is the most extreme and socially dangerous of all Bennett's misers, admitting at the outset that he has no personal interest in the trappings of luxury, but craves power as an elemental part of his makeup. He desires money, not for the material goods it can buy but for the power it can command: 'Money is power! Power! Power!' This insatiable desire animates the plot throughout, finding its ultimate expression in Flitfoot's egomaniacal rant on the will to power, excusing the need for moral judgement: 'Power! Power, my friend! Nothing like it. Luxury is nothing my friend. Power is everything. The power is not in the machinery. It's in ourselves. It's in me, me! Without me the machinery would stop.' But in a world defined by fraud, cruelty, violence and human debasement, the death of any one individual, however powerful, becomes meaningless and the machinery of corruption continues to function. The final irony is expressed in Chail's self-deluding belief that '[Flitfoot] was very kind to me.' Chail's last words are evidence that there can never be narrative closure for as long as the Punch and Judy man continues to stage his/Bennett's display of human cupidity, stupidity and violence, masked by the costume of comedy. Or, as Bennett summarises it in one final word, 'Life!'

The end of the silent film period coincided with the

beginning of the Great Depression, and it is fascinating to reflect in this context that simultaneously across the geographical extremes of Europe, three films were either in production or being planned on the subject of money, the power of capital, and the corruption of the financial system. The French director Marcel L'Herbier's updated adaptation of Emile Zola's *L'Argent* [*Money*] (1891) went on general release in 1929. Sergei Eisenstein wrote an outline scenario for a film based on Karl Marx's *Das Kapital* [*Capital*] (1867) which his diary Notes for 1928 show to have been intended to extend the narrative strategies he had developed in *Oktyabr* [*October*] (1928). Eisenstein's project fell victim to the coming of sound in much the same way as Bennett's *Punch and Judy*, although the former had also to deal with Soviet demands for a social realist aesthetic as opposed to the technical demands of Hitchcock. *L'Argent,* however, was made and viewing it provides an interesting commentary on the visual potential of *Punch and Judy*, inasmuch as both films/scenarios rest on a narrative in which money and its relation to power motivates nearly every character and underlines nearly every scene, and both end on a note despairing of redemption. There are other specific visual points of contact; both plots include an aircraft flight as modernity's response to an impending economic disaster; L'Herbier references the game of chess in a symbolically choreographed sequence of character movements across a black and white tiled spacious hall, and Bennett shows the controlling machinery of the Punch and Judy man. Whilst capital itself remains invisible, both L'Herbier and Bennett suggest its ubiquitous presence by the symbolic association of finance with cigars. L'Herbier's Saccard, the disreputable representative of the capitalist system of speculation and accumulation, is the man with the cigar. In *Punch and Judy* Bennett humorously inverts the traditional cigar = power image by associating Miss Sligo, Flitfoot's manipulatively intelligent but dedicated secretary, with a taste for cigars. Her previous invisibility in Bennett studies is regrettable on two levels. Firstly, because she is a precursor to aspects of Gracie Savotte's feminist agency in Bennett's final masterpiece *Imperial Palace* (1930). Secondly, because on the wider stage she represents the radical transformation of women's image in the material world that Virginia Woolf aimed for in her fiction but failed to achieve. All this suggests the importance of recovering and reading Bennett's scenario in the wider context of European film and fictional narratives of the period and of the impending economic implosion.

Reading *Punch and Judy* also establishes a late career link to Bennett's early serialised stories, later published as novels, in which social misdemeanours, treachery, violations of criminal law and an almost casual recourse to large amounts of money to solve problems, are a prominent feature. *The Grand Babylon Hotel* (1902), *The Gates of Wrath* (1903), *Teresa of Watling Street* (1904), *Hugo* (1906) and *The Sinews of War* (1906), co-authored with Eden Phillpotts, all contain their fair share of exceptionally rich, morally repugnant and murderous characters whose role is to highlight what Peter McDonald reads as a very definitely intended 'surreptitious symbolic war against the privileged and the governing classes' (*British literary culture*, p.110). At the same time McDonald also notes Bennett's somewhat paradoxical tendency to invalidate his socialist/liberal political agenda with a commercially inflected judgement not to offend his target middle class readership with any too blatant portrayal of, or reform programme for, the undoubted social and political discontent of the time.

Punch and Judy is heir to this conflicted outlook, but with clear evidence of a new willingness to expose the continuing financial corruption of post-World War I London city life, and partly to do so by referencing real events and naming real individuals. There was indeed a battle in the 1920s to monopolise the existing highly profitable supply of electricity by a number of small companies which led to the formation of the London Power Company and the building of several large generating stations similar to that in which Flitfoot meets his nemesis. The growing influence of American capital on European financial and business institutions is hinted at when the American entrepreneur, John Champ Curtiss, introduces the name of Yerkes as a model for structuring takeovers: 'Yerkes came over from New York to London and took hold of London's underground railways.' Charles Tyson Yerkes (1837-1905) led a colourful financial career in the U.S.A., involving financial speculation using public money, blackmail, prison, political bribery, before it culminated in his taking a controlling hand in the development of the London underground railway system. Bennett, an admirer and reviewer of several Theodore Dreiser novels, would have been aware of Yerkes's fictionalised life-story as the unscrupulous tycoon Frank Cowperwood in Dreiser's *The Financier* (1912) and *The Titan* (1914). Curtiss's valorisation of Yerkes provides evidence of Bennett's awareness of the continuity of historical corruption in financial life. In McDonald's terms, however, there has to be some doubt as to whether even a contemporary reader/viewer, let alone one in the twenty-first century, would uncover the symbolic reference to the dynamics of a corrupt business class. The Hitchcock who filmed a sound version of Galsworthy's play *The Skin Game* in 1931, with its portrayal of a conflict between brash new industrialism and established rural conservative values, might have been the ideal partner in any such overt exposure. Sharing Bennett's love of dogs – he included them in many of his English films – he certainly showed no less compunction than Bennett in killing them for artistic ends, whether it was a Jack Russell puppy blown up by a bomb in *Sabotage* (1936, adapted from Joseph Conrad's *The Secret Agent*) or strangling an inquisitive pet in *Rear Window* (1954). Incidentally, Bennett's callow treatment of the Chow, Toby, in *Punch and Judy* sounds a rare but remarkably strong echo of a similar gratuitously vindictive dog poisoning in his 1905 serial 'Lord Dover. The Strange Adventures of a Spendthrift Peer'. Further tantalising links of the possibilities inherent in a co-operative Hitchcock/Bennett film venture are found in Steven Jacobs's 2007 study *The Wrong House: The Architecture of Alfred Hitchcock*, in which he traces Hitchcock's visual interest in large kitchens, in films such as *Young and Innocent* (1937) through to *The Man Who Knew Too Much* (1956), back to reading Bennett's *The Grand Babylon Hotel*.

In the event, there is no happy ending for Bennett's story in the reel world. Rather than looking forward to the coming world of sound film, *Punch and Judy* maintains its affinity with *Vanity Fair*, whilst violating popular cinema's desire for happy endings and colluding with Thackeray's pessimistic refusal to endorse marriage as a conventional closure. *'Ah! Vanitas Vanitatum!'*/'Life!'

JOHN SHAPCOTT
University of Keele

ACKNOWLEDGEMENTS

My first thanks go to Jacques Eldin, Arnold Bennett's son-in-law, who very graciously gave his permission for this first ever publication of *Punch and Judy*. The original holograph is held in the La Fayette Butler Collection of Arnold Bennett Publishing Correspondence and Manuscripts, Special Collections Library, Pennsylvania State University Libraries, and I gratefully acknowledge the University's permission to publish my transcription of the holograph. In particular I would like to thank Sandra Stelts, Curator of Rare Books and Manuscripts, who has been a helpful correspondent since first approached in February 2007.

As a long-term admirer of Margaret Drabble's fiction and non-fiction it is a particular pleasure to acknowledge her generous contribution of a sparkling Foreword to this volume.

I would like to thank Martin Laux for his reading of the entire manuscript, and for his subsequent helpful suggestions.

Once again I am indebted to Nicholas Redman for making available material from his personal archive, including contemporary newspaper and periodical references to Bennett's film work.

Whilst every effort has been made to trace the holders of copyright material the publisher would be grateful to know of any omissions. In this connection I would like to thank Linda Shaughnessy (A. P. Watt, Literary Film and Television Agents) for her help in the search for any remaining film company copyrights.

This book is dedicated to Linda Shapcott, whose patient and determined transcription skills have helped make its present publication possible.

BIBLIOGRAPHY

Barr, Charles. *English Hitchcock.* Moffat, Scotland: Cameron & Holliss, 1999.

Bennett, Arnold. *Literary Taste. How To Form It.* London: New Age Press, 1909.

The Regent. Leek: Churnet Valley Books, 2006.

The Old Wives' Tale. Leek: Churnet Valley Books, 2008.

The Price of Love. Churnet Valley Books, 2006.

The Savour of Life. London: Cassell, 1928.

Piccadilly. A Story of the Film. London: Readers Library Publishing Company, 1929.

Imperial Palace. London: Cassell, 1930.

Letters of Arnold Bennett Vol.I. Edited. James Hepburn. London: Oxford U.P., 1966

Letters of Arnold Bennett Vol.III. Edited. James Hepburn. London: Oxford U.P., 1970.

The Journal of Arnold Bennett. New York: The Literary Guild 1933.

'The Film "Story"', *Sight and Sound*. London: BFI, 1954.

Bordwell, David. *Narration in the Fiction Film.* London: Routledge, 1997.

Dixon, Bryony. *100 Silent Films.* London: British Film Institute, 2011.

Donald, James, Anne Friedberg & Laura Marcus. *Close Up 1927-1933. Cinema* and *Modernism.* London: Cassell, 1998.

Drabble, Margaret *Arnold Bennett.* London: Weidenfeld and Nicolson, 1974.

Gledhill, Christine. *Reframing British Cinema. 1918-1928*. London: BFI, 2003.

Hepburn, James. *Arnold Bennett. The Critical Heritage.* London: Routledge & Kegan Paul, 1981.

Jacobs, Steven. *The Wrong House: The Architecture of Alfred Hitchcock.* Rotterdam: 010 Publishers, 2007.

Low, Rachel. *The History of the British Film 1918-1929.* London: George Allen & Unwin, 1971.

Marcus, Laura. *The Tenth Muse. Writing about Cinema in the Modernist Period.* Oxford: Oxford U.P., 2007.

McDonald, Peter D. *British literary culture and publishing practice 1880-1914*. Cambridge: Cambridge U.P., 1997.

Rotha, Paul. *The Film Till Now: A Survey of the Cinema.* London: Jonathan Cape, 1930.

Thackeray, William. *Vanity Fair.* Oxford: Oxford U.P., 1983.

Wells. H. G. *The King Who Was A King:* London: Ernest Benn, 1929.

Williams, Keith. *H. G. Wells, Modernity and the Movies.* Liverpool: Liverpool U.P., 2007.

FILMOGRAPHY

Chaplin, Charles *The Circus.* Warner Brothers, mk2 DVD, 1970.
Dupont, E. A. *Piccadilly.* British Film Institute DVD, 2003.
Vaudeville (There is no current British DVD available, but a plot synopsis, critical commentary and technical information can be accessed on www.silentsaregolden.com.)
L'Herbier, Marcel. *L'Argent.* Eureka Entertainment DVD, 2008.
Macpherson, Kenneth *Borderline.* British Film Institute DVD, 2007.
Murnau, F. W. *Faust.* Eureka Entertainment DVD, 2006.
The Last Laugh. Eureka Entertainment DVD, 2008.

NOTE ON THE TEXT

The text reproduced in this volume is as nearly as possible an exact transcription of the original holograph, held in the 'La Fayette Butler Collection of Arnold Bennett Publishing Correspondence and Manuscripts, 1903-1931', at Pennsylvania State University, U.S.A.

Parts I and III are transcribed from the original typescripts, incorporating Bennett's handwritten amendments, corrections and deletions. The exception to this general rule concerns the reference to the Negro puppet character in Part I. Bennett crossed out all references to this character, but it is re-instated in the present text, along with other crossed-through passages, within square brackets, in the interests of future scholarship.

Part II is transcribed/deciphered from Bennett's often challenging handwriting, together with his frequent practice of inserting extra text in margins and squeezed between lines. In general the original punctuation and spelling have been retained, with only minor corrections to obvious errors. The bank manager's title appears in the standardised format of General Manager whereas Bennett uses a mixture of upper and lower case and hyphenated words. Similarly the variant spellings of whisky/whiskey have been standardised as whisky. Numbers have been hyphenated e.g. thirty-five. Foreign phrases have been italicised.

Where individual words or phrases proved resistant to interpretation, even after resorting to magnification, a decision was reached on the basis of context, grammar, cursive style and, over an extended period of time, familiarity with other examples of Bennett's handwriting. There remain a very few instances, however, where the final decision rests on an educated guess.

Anna May Wong, who starred in Arnold Bennett's film Piccadilly.

Arnold Bennett in later years.

PUNCH AND JUDY

PART I

THE FILM SCENARIO

The "Punch and Judy" man, with his dog and his wife, comes into the Square wheeling his collapsible little sentry-box and his apparatus. He sets up the box, and arranges the curtains behind. Within is a large chest, which he at last opens. It contains all the wooden figures: Punch, Judy, their baby, Scaramouch, the doctor, the Negro, Polly, the policeman, the chief-constable, the hangman, and the horse. He pulls them out of the chest and throws them down anyhow. They are nothing but ugly and misshapen lifeless dolls. They have no vitality whatever. It seems impossible that they ever should have any vitality or even interest.

The "Punch and Judy" man whose head is lower than the proscenium opening, begins his opening talk.

All the above is seen from the inside of the sentry-box.

Then we see the Square, with people, especially children, gathering to watch the Punch and Judy show. The dog stays inside, but the wife is outside, preparing to make a collection.

The show starts.

Glimpses from time to time of the working of the figures from the inside.

The figures, as seen by the audience, now have a most

surprising vitality. They are alive. Impossible to believe that they are mere pieces of wood. Their monstrous faces are wooden and show no expression. Nevertheless they seem to show expression. The audience – and not only the children – are convinced of their reality, and follow their fortunes just as though they were human beings. It is as if a miracle had happened; yet no miracle has happened. The children and the adults all laugh at the misfortunes and the deaths of the wooden dolls, and thoroughly enjoy the murderous triumphant wickedness of Punch.

The film sticks closely to the usual Punch and Judy show,[1] which is full of slapstick comedy and contains also some pretty good jokes. (Herewith is the latest book describing the Punch and Judy performance[2] in detail.) It is divided into nine episodes, – or less, as may be convenient.

1. The dog, which bites Punch's nose, and which is the origin of most of the trouble.
2. Scaramouch,[3] the servant of the dog's owner. Punch grumbles about the behaviour of the dog, which has ruined his beautiful nose. Punch and Scaramouch have a fight, in which at first Punch gets some hard blows, but which ends by Punch knocking Scaramouch's head clean off.
3. Judy and the baby. Judy leaves Punch to mind the baby. While nursing the baby, Punch lets it fall. The baby cries and won't stop crying. Punch, angry at the noise, throws the baby out of the window. Judy reappears and reproaches Punch for throwing the baby out of the window. They fight. Judy beats Punch. Then Punch knocks her senseless. He cannot believe she is dead. But she is dead, and when Punch realises this he throws her out of the window after the baby.
4. Polly, the maid-servant. Polly is a very nice and beautiful girl. She supplies the idyllic element in the story. She loves

Punch. They dance together. Polly departs.

5. The horse. Punch attempts to ride it. Fails. Succeeds; and is thrown heavily.

6. The doctor, who is summoned to attend to Punch's injuries. Punch takes offence at him. There is a fight. Punch kills the doctor. This episode contains the chief joke of the comedy. Punch says afterwards in self-defence: "Of course I killed him. If I hadn't killed him, he, being a doctor, would have killed me."

7. [The Negro.[4] Punch begins to ring a very loud bell in his triumph. The Negro is a servant sent by his master to protest against the noise. They fight. Punch knocks the Negro senseless.]

8. The policeman and the chief constable arrive to enquire into Punch's murders. Punch kills both of them. [The Negro, however, is not dead, and, while Punch is absent, he moves the bodies of the other two from the place where Punch had left them. Slapstick, ending with the murder of the Negro by Punch.]

9. The hangman arrives with the gallows. Punch gets the better of him by persuading him to show by example how the head of a criminal is put into the noose. Punch is left finally triumphant with the dead hangman by his side.

The Punch and Judy show over, or nearly over, Punch changes into a human being, Henry Flitfoot, the hero of a story about real people – not puppets.

Just as the movements of Punch the puppet are actuated by cords or other devices, so – if the Director finds it advisable – might the movements of Flitfoot seem sometimes (in crises) to be actuated by mysterious cords, pulling at his hands etc.

The foregoing makes a sort of prologue to Part II. Its mood is light, jolly, funny, and at the same time ruthless. The character of Punch is the embodiment of the instinct for self-satisfaction, of seeking for power and mastery, of the determination to be the top dog – at any cost. Punch is continually actuated by this single instinct, – the *will-to-power* which leaves him the conqueror in his own world – subject to one fatal condition, a condition that emerges later.

We now come to a story of a group of human beings, of whom the chief is a character driven onwards always by the ruthless Punch instinct. Call this man X. X is human enough, amusing and jolly, but in any crisis, the Punch-instinct sways him and forces him to act ruthlessly. He is ambitious of course; but he is more than ambitious; he is the very symbol of the *will-to-power*. Herein is the essence of the character.

I have thought of a number of episodes in his life which would suggest the story of Punch (and of Judy); but I will not detail them until I know whether the general form of the film strikes you as suitable. I should certainly have fewer murders in the human story than there are in Punch and Judy. Indeed I should have only one murder. But there would be acts of X which lead to disaster, and even death, for people with whom he is brought into close contact.

The incident of the doctor, for instance, might be represented in terms of real life. An authoritative doctor, bent on treating X when seriously ill in a particular manner, might well be murdered by the restive X, who would recover and proceed on his course of triumph.

Money being the source of power, X would naturally make himself a millionaire. He would stick at nothing to do so. He would be overbearing with his wife. His neglect of her might lead to her death. Similarly with their child. But X

OPPOSITE PAGE — In Arnold Bennett's *Punch and Judy* the dog is Toby, the horse is the aeroplane and the doctor is Sir Andrew Forfar.

would continue, going from one success to another; never beaten, always triumphant by reason of his total lack of scruple. He is a great man, but he is great in evil. He is as much the victim of his master-instinct as his companions are the victims of it. He may fight against his tremendous instinct, but it is too strong for him every time. (His instinct might be represented occasionally in the story by strings which move his limbs as strings move the limbs of a marionette. Room for effective symbolism here!) Nothing but his humour, his gaiety, his sense of fun, his amusing resourcefulness in a difficulty, makes him tolerable.

At last, after having accomplished deeds which cause him to be suspected of crime, he does something of which the law is bound to take notice, and he is apprehended and accused. He is very rich, dazzlingly successful, and utterly unscrupulous. The prosecuting barrister, a celebrated K.C., is his enemy, for the reason that this man is very interested in Polly, who is the pure and romantic element in the whole story and who loves X in her quiet and nun-like way. In a supreme struggle X is able to turn the tables on the barrister. [whose career, though he is perfectly innocent, is ruined. X comes out of the immense ordeal unscathed, his reputation cleared, though he is suspected by all. His triumph is more prodigious than ever. Nothing has been able to touch him.

Then he dies, by accident. His reputation is a burst balloon. Death has completely destroyed it. Alive, he had the innumerable flattering friends common to all millionaires. Dead he has none. His body lies solitary in his palace. Only the figure of Polly, forgiving, loving, pitiful, relieves the tragedy of the scene.]

"I don't know anything about grandees, sir. But they say he's a widower and the richest man in the Mansions."

"You can go," said Hilfort.

The attendant went.

Hilfort perched his silk hat on the end of his walking-stick and gleefully whirled the hat round and round like a conjurer.

"Old Josh is the electric king of London. He has a flat in the Mansions, and here's his daughter's dog! Providence is in this affair!"

"But why," asked Chail once almost apologetically, "why did you say that I killed the animal?"

"Well, you see. You haven't got any reputation to keep up here. I have. I don't want to be known as a dog-killer. I must be the dog-saviour. No harm to you. Besides, your conscience is clear. That's the chief thing. And hang it all, man, haven't I made a hero of you!"

"I see," said Chail feebly.

"Where's the Buff book?" Hilfort snatched at the volume of the telephone and rapidly turned over its pages. "Veterinary Surgeons. Um! Um! Um! Sloane 99 double nine.... That Mr. Thatcher? Will you please come to Sir Joshua Marsington's flat, Belgrave Mansions, at once to examine a dog who has had an attack of mistaken identity. Yes. Mistaken identity. Well-known canine disease. It's very urgent. Thank you." Hilfort hung up the receiver. "And now my friend, I must leave you. Stay and have a drink before you go. I'll buy those [illegible] shares."

Hilfort courageously picked up the dog, who was patted on the head.

"I say," said he, dropping the dog on to the table. "Lend me a penknife."

"A penknife?" Chail had refilled his glass and was drinking.

"Yes. It's for the dog. Quick!" With a comical gesture of distress he cut a ragged slit in the leg of his trousers. "A new pair," said he. "But a great cause is worth a great sacrifice!" He snapped the blade of the penknife and threw it negligently back to Chail.

"Goodbye, Chail."

Then Henry Hilfort hesitated to take the penknife. He held back his hands, but it seemed to him as if invisible cords were drawing them irresistibly towards the penknife. This strange phenomenon of being compelled to do something which one part of his mind [illegible] was in no way familiar to him. He took the penknife; and [illegible]

A page of Bennett's manuscript, reproduced by kind permission of Pennsylvania State University Libraries.

PUNCH AND JUDY

PART II

THE NOVEL

CHAPTER I

Belgrave Mansions, Mayfair. A block of service-flats; not a very large building; but flats of the highest class. Time 6.30 p.m. In the entrance hall a card hung on the lift-door: "Lift out of order".

A young woman as elegant, fashionable and expensive as the building and the district came hurrying into the hall and seeing the notice on the lift-door, walked up the stairs which surrounded the well of the lift.

She was followed by a dog, a chow[1] – rather old. The dog, of an inquisitive disposition, stayed to examine various corners of the hall.

A dark personable man of thirty-five well dressed in City style next came smiling into the hall. Perceiving the notice, he frowned.

"Again!" said he. "And these are supposed to be the swellest flats in London. Get away."

The last two words were addressed rather angrily to the dog, which was conducting an enquiry into the shining boots of Mr. Henry Flitfoot, chartered accountant and income-tax expert.

The dog growled. Flitfoot raised his walking-stick. He did not like dogs, and evidently this particular dog did not like him. Flitfoot began to climb the noble stairs. The dog, resentful of the stick, went after him, still growling. On the first landing Flitfoot raised his stick again at the animal. On the second landing, while Flitfoot was finding his latchkey, the dog frankly treated the chartered accountant as an enemy. Flitfoot, annoyed and defensive, managed to open the front-door of his flat and slip in. But the dog slipped in with him.

"Very well! If you want trouble!" said Flitfoot menacingly, and shut the door.

He backed into a sitting room, the dog yelping around him. There, with sudden decision and careful aim, he savagely kicked the dog on the head. The dog, a moment earlier the image of irritated vivacity, lay lifeless. Mr. Flitfoot shoved the body with his foot into a corner, and, all cheerful smiles back again, sat down and lit a cigarette. He had dropped his stick, and now he deposited his silk hat. He did not read; he did not look out of the window at the wide world. He was content just to sit and smoke and smile and gaze at the inanimate dog.

The room was very plainly and sparsely furnished.

A liveried attendant entered.

"Mr. Jeremy Chail".

Mr. Chail entered. The attendant vanished.

"Hallo, Chail." Mr. Flitfoot greeted him warmly, but without getting up from his chair. "Glad to see you. Sit down, and have a drink."

The differences between the two men were striking. Flitfoot was young (about thirty-six); Chail was over fifty. Flitfoot was smart; Chail was only neat. Flitfoot was gay; Chail was subdued. Flitfoot was at ease; Chail was constrained. Flitfoot was careless and challenging; Chail was timid and ingratiating. Flitfoot had the air of one accustomed to give orders - which were obeyed; Chail had the air of one accustomed to receive orders and to obey them quickly. Flitfoot had the air of triumph; Chail had the air of defeat.

Chail also had the air of one accustomed to console himself in defeat by means of whisky, for he handled a glass like an expert and drank with gusto.

Chail had taken an arm-chair which had lost a castor. It rocked. Flitfoot rose, screwed up some sheets of notepaper and stuffed them under the leg.

"There! The bereaved leg is comforted."

"You're rather Spartan here," Chail ventured.

"Yes."

"But your office is so magnificent."

"Ah! Office is to impress rich clients. Here I'm at home and I've no interest in luxury. I only took this little flat for one reason. The reason is on my notepaper."

He showed a sheet of the notepaper: "Belgrave Mansions, W.1."

"But," Chail persisted, "you're a masquerader. If you don't want luxury why do you want money?"

"Money is power! Power! Power!" Flitfoot stood up as he repeated the magic word and laughed. Then with fierce seriousness:

"I want power. I must have it."

"You'd like to be a millionaire?"

"I will be a millionaire."

"Well, if you followed my tip," said Chail, "you made a nice little sum last week. The shares went up £3. Say you bought 1,000 shares for the rise, you're richer by £3,000. And you promised me a present if the thing came off."

"It didn't come off; so I've no present for you, my dear fellow," said Flitfoot lightly.

"Didn't come off?"

"No. Because I didn't buy. You see, you may be a confidential clerk with one of the biggest stockbroking firms in the City. And you may hear of a good thing. But I had to test you first. Couldn't take risks. Well, I've tested you, and I'll act on your *next* tip, and if it's as good as the first one you'll get a very nice present."

"May I ask how much?"

"Depends on the result. Now I see you have another tip for me. Out with it."

"Tidal Power shares.[2] They're at 11. They'll go to 14 at least certainly. There's going to be a push."

"Right! Say no more. I'll buy a couple of thousand, and if you're wrong I'll kill you like I killed that dog." Flitfoot laughed again more loudly. "Have another."

Chail had another, while gazing alarmed at the dog.

Flitfoot rang the bell.

"He declared himself my enemy," Flitfoot cheerfully explained about the dog. "He is now at peace."

The attendant entered, very smartly.

Said Flitfoot to the attendant:

"Remove that animal, please. His mission in life is finished. He has earned a place in the dustbin. He attacked me and followed me into this room, which is strictly private. My friend here pluckily saved me from him. One masterly kick!–"

The dog raised its head feebly.

"He isn't dead, sir," said the attendant, and added: "That's Miss Marsington's dog. She's been enquiring about him and she's in a terrible state."

"And who is Miss Marsington?"

"Fourth floor, sir. Daughter of Sir Joshua Marsington."

"Surely not the electric light grandee?"

"I don't know anything about grandees, sir. But they say he's a widower and the richest man in the Mansions."

"You can go," said Flitfoot.

The attendant went.

Flitfoot perched his silk hat on the end of his walking-stick and gleefully whirled the hat round and round like a conjurer.

"Old Josh is the electricity king of London. He has a flat in the Mansions, and here's his daughter's dog! Providence is in this affair!"

"But why," asked Chail almost apologetically, "why did you say that *I* killed the animal?"

"Well, you see. *You* haven't got any reputation to keep up here. *I* have. I don't want to be known as a dog-killer. I must be the dog-saviour. No harm to you. Besides, your conscience is clear. That's the chief thing. And hang it all, man, haven't I made a hero of you!"

"I see," said Chail feebly.

"Where's the Buff book?"[3] Flitfoot snatched at the volume by the telephone and rapidly turned over its pages. "Veterinary Surgeons. Um! Um! Um! Sloane 99 double nine.... "That Mr. Thatcher? Will you please come to Sir Joshua Marsington's flat, Belgrave Mansions, at once to examine a dog which has had an attack of mistaken identity. Yes, mistaken identity. Well-known canine disease. It's very urgent. Thank you." Flitfoot hung up the receiver. "And now my friend, I must leave you. Have another drink before you go. I'll buy a few of those Tidal Power shares."

Flitfoot courageously picked up the dog, who growled and was hit on the head.

"I say," said he, dropping the dog on to the table, "hand me a penknife."

"A penknife?" Chail had refilled his glass and was drinking.

"Yes. It isn't for the dog. Quick!"

Then Henry Flitfoot hesitated to take the penknife. He held back his hands, but it seemed to him as if invisible cords were drawing them irresistibly towards the penknife. This strange phenomenon of being compelled to do something which one part of his mind desired not to do was familiar to him.

He took the penknife, and opening it with a comical gesture of distress he cut a ragged slit on the seat of his trousers.

"A new pair," said he. "Very expensive. But a great cause is worth a great sacrifice!"

He snapped the blade of the penknife and threw it negligently back to Chail.

"Goodbye, Chail."

Flitfoot seized the dog again in his arms, pushed Chail in front of him through the door, and hurried upstairs.

CHAPTER II

Still holding the dog as a mother holds a baby, Mr. Flitfoot rang the bell of the Marsington flat. The door was opened by a maid.

"Please tell Miss Marsington that a man has called about a dog."

The maid cried as if in ecstasy.

"Oh! Darling Toby!"

And she ran within, taking the card which Flitfoot handed to her.

"Yes," said Flitfoot to himself. "Darling Toby! If he's so darling as all that I'd better do a bit more to my darling trousers."

And with his finger he lengthened considerably the damage to his trousers. Then he blithely followed the maid into the flat, which was very much larger and infinitely grander than his own. At the entrance to a drawing-room a young woman rushed to meet him. She was well-dressed, a blonde, not particularly tall, not startlingly beautiful; indeed critical members of her sex might have described her looks and demeanour as being a little on the homely side; but in her face with its warm, melting eyes was an expression of kindliness, of acquiescence, of submission which instantly attracted the self-willed tyrant in Henry Flitfoot.

"It's marvellous!" he thought. "This is the mild and yielding creature of my dreams. If only she's an only child ...."

"Thank you. Thank you. How good you are, Mr. Flitfoot!" said the young woman in a low emotional tone, and took the dog and caressed and kissed it.

"Do come in, please."

Flitfoot came in.

"I'm afraid," he remarked sadly, though his eyes shone with triumph, "I'm afraid there was a little accident to your darling Toby. Not quite my fault. It happened before I could prevent it."

He gave her the version of the episode which he had previously given to the flunkey.

"But I think no serious harm is done," he finished.

"I'm sure not," said the young woman, carefully placing Toby in his basket. Then to the hovering maid: "Some milk, and put a little brandy in it."

The maid ran off.

"And in order to be on the safe side," said Flitfoot, "I ventured to telephone for a vet. He ought to be here in a minute or two."

"How thoughtful of you! I feel you must *love* dogs, Mr. Flitfoot, as I do."

"I adore dogs," replied Flitfoot. "I should always suspect a man who didn't care for dogs."

The maid returned with a bowl. Toby lapped it.

"He needed food, poor thing," said the young woman.

"That's just what I thought," said Flitfoot.

At this point Sir Joshua Marsington came hurriedly and fussily into the room: a man of short, thick body, with fingers to match. He was aged about sixty. His face gave the impression that he was never convinced of the genuineness of his own importance in the world of affairs; he had made a considerable reputation in the City by keeping silent when he could not decide what he ought to say. On the present occasion he immediately beheld a spectacle which his daughter so far had been deprived of, namely, a back view of Henry Flitfoot. The spectacle amazed him and brought him to a very sudden standstill.

"Father," said the young woman modestly. "This is Mr.

Flitfoot, who has been kind about poor Toby. Mr. Flitfoot, my father, Sir Joshua."

Sir Joshua advanced, in silence.

"Whatever is the matter, dad?"

Sir Joshua beckoned his daughter, who then for the first time cast eyes on the enormous rent in Flitfoot's trousers.

"But he's bitten you – and you never said a word!"

"He certainly was a little active," replied Flitfoot airily. "But he didn't bite *me* – only my trousers. It's nothing. I'd forgotten it. I ought only to apologise for appearing here in such a state."

"Apologise?" said the young woman. "I'm so ashamed.... and you've been so wonderful about it all! Toby, you naughty, naughty dog!"

"Julia," said Sir Joshua, when he had heard the story, shaken hands and offered solemn excuses to Flitfoot. "I've warned you before about this dog being dangerous. He's old and he's entitled to die."

"Sir Joshua!" Flitfoot protested. "I honestly don't think he's dangerous. If he could talk he would say he got into a mix-up and was only defending himself."

"In any case, Julia," said Sir Joshua, "you must pay for a new suit for Mr. Flitfoot – and you must pay for it out of your own private income."

Flitfoot caught the last words with joyous interest.

"Not at all!" said he laughing. "I wouldn't hear of it. I shall charge the new suit as a professional expense in my income-tax return."

Sir Joshua's dull face lit up.

"Ah!" he said. "This monstrous income-tax is strangling trade."

"Quite," said Flitfoot. "The fact is, my job is to stop income-tax from strangling trade. It happens that I'm a chartered accountant, Sir Joshua. I used to do a general business, but now I specialise in protecting the poor income-tax payer against a rapacious and unscrupulous State. I find it most profitable. So I think I can work the trousers item."

"Very interesting!" said Sir Joshua seriously. "Do stay and have a drink."

"Most kind of you," said Flitfoot. "But I'm late for an appointment now. If Miss Marsington would allow me to call tomorrow and see how poor Toby is getting on –"

Both father and daughter were rather effusive - the daughter particularly. So goodbyes were said. Miss Marsington might have been a queen, for Flitfoot backed out of the room – in order to hide that which was no proper sight for a lady to whom his bright eyes showed that he had conceived the liveliest admiration for her.

"The vet is certain to be here in a moment," said he reassuringly, at parting.

And on the doormat he met the veterinary surgeon, Mr. Thatcher, arriving.

"It was I who telephoned to you, Mr. Thatcher," said Flitfoot. "I'm a friend of the family. I'll give you a tip. Sir Joshua feels a strong desire to attend the dog's funeral."

CHAPTER III

Back in his own flat, Flitfoot telephoned to his office in the City. The call was answered by his private secretary. Miss Sligo was a slim, worn, eager woman of forty, at once sardonic and laconic.

"That you, Sligo? The boss speaking."

"Yes."

"Anybody else there?"

"No. They've all gone long since."

"Why have you stayed?"

"Oh, I'm clearing up. I shall be here for some time yet if you need anything."

"I only want you to be at the office early tomorrow and ring up the brokers and buy 10,000 Tidal Power Company shares. Yes, Tidal Power."

"Which brokers?"

"All four of them. Tell each of 'em to buy 2,500 shares for me. Don't want everyone to know everything. That clear?"

"Yes."

CHAPTER IV

Mr. Henry Flitfoot occupied a considerable suite of offices in the City. The rooms in it were furnished in a manner to indicate that the chief was not a man to spare money in the pursuit of a 100 per cent business efficiency. His own private office, where he sat on the following afternoon, at his large severe American desk of which the drawers locked themselves automatically by the turn of a single lever, was the most expensively efficient of all the rooms. The desk had formidable rivals in the shape of a consultation table, file-cabinets, a cigar-cabinet, a cigarette-cabinet, a reference-bookcase, a newspaper-stand and chairs to suit various moods and various physiques. The general impression given was that, minutes and even seconds being golden, every mechanical contrivance had been collected so that the precious metal should not be wasted.

Flitfoot had little belief in the value of these devices, but, being a cynic, he had a great belief in their power to influence the opinions of his clients concerning himself. Frightened muddlers beheld them with ignorant admiration, while the competent were inspired by them to yearn after a new perfection.

Flitfoot used the telephone.

With extraordinary promptness Miss Ruth Sligo, carrying documents, responded to the summons. If Miss Sligo was efficient - and she was - her clothes gave no sign of this quality; she was dressed anyhow; she had other ways of showing efficiency, and little time for adornment. She enjoyed no private life. Her whole existence was monopolised by Flitfoot and his office. She received a comparatively small salary, and never suggested a rise. She was naught but a secretary; other individuals in the establishment earned far more than she did, and considered themselves far more important. But she was quite content in the assurance that their importance was far inferior to hers. She knew that her employer's confidence in her was complete. She knew that she alone was indispensable. The sense of indispensability was her rich recompense for long hours, fatiguing labour, narrow means, lack of sleep and lack of love. She was grim, but she was happy. She had accomplished a feat which Flitfoot himself never would and never could accomplish - she had acquired power without money. She had proved to her own satisfaction that the most dominant and severe employee is the one who, entrusted with secrets and keeping them, asks no favours in return.

"You haven't brought me those contract-notes," said Flitfoot. Saying no word, Miss Sligo handed to him four contract-notes for the purchase of 2,500 Tidal Power shares each.

Flitfoot examined them and dropped them into a drawer.

"And my letters?"

Saying no word, Miss Sligo handed his letters to Flitfoot for signature. As he rapidly signed them she with equal rapidity blotted them.

"I'm in a hurry," said Flitfoot.

Miss Sligo said nothing, another secret of her strength lay in the fact that she never showed curiosity.

"I'm going to have tea with Sir Joseph Marsington," said Flitfoot, still signing.

Miss Sligo said nothing.

"And his daughter," said Flitfoot.

Miss Sligo said nothing.

"She means well, but she's quite, quite uninteresting," said Flitfoot, who had the habit of talking to Miss Sligo as though she couldn't hear, or didn't exist.

"In fact she's a stupid little thing," said Flitfoot.

"But not more stupid than Sir Joshua," said Miss Sligo very surprisingly, with the utmost callousness. From time to time she did make startling remarks.

"Oh!" said Flitfoot, glancing up and ceasing to sign. "Who told you that?"

"I know Mr. Meacham and Mr. Meacham is Sir Joshua's 'Sligo'"

"Oh!" said Flitfoot. "And how do you know Mr. Meacham?"

"Well, he's kept late and I'm kept late and I see him at the Bagdad Café at Amen Corner[1] at night when it's empty."

"And so Mr. Meacham has told you that Sir Joshua is stupid?"

"No. I just gathered it." Miss Sligo was characteristically laconic.

"Then have you any theory to explain Sir Joshua's great position in the City?"

"Yes. His wife had pots of money; he had the handling of it. One or two flukes at first; and then he found a clever Scotchman named Forfar who runs one or two of his companies for him and whose advice he takes."

Miss Sligo was still laconic.

"And does this Mr. Meacham know who *you* are?"

"He does not. He thinks I'm a manicurist." Miss Sligo was still laconic.

"Then don't undeceive him," said Flitfoot.

"I shan't. I keep myself *to* myself."

"And so she has a fortune of her own, eh?"

"Who? Julia? Yes."

"So her name's Julia?"

"Only child," said Miss Sligo, even more laconic.

"Perhaps stupid, but worth encouraging."

Flitfoot, who was signing the last letter, looked up. But Miss Sligo went to a cupboard and produced his hat, stick and gloves.

"That's all," she said.

Flitfoot departed hurriedly.

CHAPTER V

Before going upstairs to take tea with the Marsingtons that afternoon, Mr. Flitfoot called in at his own flat, arranged his hair, his necktie and his handkerchief, and then he sat down for a few minutes to skim through a small book, which he had brought with him, entitled "Dogs and all about them."

The Marsington door was opened, as on the previous day, by Julia's own maid, whom Flitfoot now familiarly and cheerfully greeted as an old acquaintance.

"And how is dear Toby today?" he enquired with smiling, hopeful anxiety. "Able to sit up?"

"Yes, sir. Much better thank you, sir." The girl could not help smiling.

"Interested in his food?"

"Oh yes, sir. The veterinary surgeon sent down a pill for him this morning; but he seemed so bright that Miss Julia would not give it him."

"They say it's best to leave well alone."

In the drawing-room the maid said:

"Miss Julia will be here in a moment, sir."

And left Flitfoot alone.

Glancing around, he saw a gilt pill-box on the mantelpiece. Doubtless the pill for Toby, designed by the obliging vet to lead to Toby's funeral. Flitfoot hesitated but those invisible cords pulled his hands towards the box and he seized and examined it. He had just time to shut the box and slip it into his pocket when Julia entered.

Julia apparently made no effort to conceal her pleasure at the sight of Henry Flitfoot. The truth was, however, that she was making a tremendous effort to conceal it, but the effort completely failed.

"I'm so relieved to hear that Toby is out of danger," said Flitfoot, shaking hands.

"Yes, my maid's just told me how kindly you enquired."

A pompous and condescending flunkey of the Mansions served tea.

"We won't wait for father. He's always late," said Julia.

The two sat down in intimacy, and Julia, obviously in a state of trembling felicity, poured out tea. As for Flitfoot, his demeanour was intended to prove, and did prove to Julia, that this was the happiest moment of his whole life. He bowed towards Julia, and talked softly to the accompaniment of a variety of smiles. If Julia opened her mouth he stopped suddenly, with deference, as if attaching the very highest importance to anything she might utter.

"Dogs are very like human beings," said Julia simply.

Flitfoot received this remark as the startling revelation of a profound verity which had never before occurred to his inferior intelligence. He gazed at Julia in admiration.

"How true that is!" said he, and then, after a suitable pause, went on talking.

"You must love dogs," said Julia.

"I told you I did."

"You know such a lot about them," said Julia.

"Not really," said Flitfoot with modesty. "But of course if you *do* like animals you manage to pick up a few notions about them."

"I expect you keep dogs yourself?"

"Not in a London flat," said Flitfoot.

"No?" said Julia. Then, with a certain sturdiness: "When *I'm* in a London flat, my dog has to be in a London flat too. We are never separated. This morning father absolutely insisted that Toby should be sent to the country; but I said that if Toby went I should go too, and father gave in at that." Julia's sudden vivacity somewhat alarmed Mr. Flitfoot, who began to perceive that his estimate of her character had been overestimating her submissiveness. He collected his forces.

"You're very ruthless," he said quietly.

"Oh *no*!" she protested, both shocked and pleased by his accusation.

"Excuse me! I've no right to .."

"Yes, you have. I'd like to hear your views."

"If you were an old hag," said Flitfoot, "I could understand it. But when a young and beautiful girl puts a dog before a human being–"

"But I don't."

"No? Then why would you sooner part from your father than from your dog? Nobody cares if a faded spinster gives up her duties in life to a dog or a cat. It's quite common. But you! When *you* do it, a man feels humiliated. He gets jealous. I do believe I feel jealous of Toby myself."

Julia was silent.

"I've annoyed you. I'm sorry," Flitfoot murmured wistfully. "If I give you my honest opinion it's only because I admire your intelligence. A man's never sincere with a woman who's stupid."

"But I prefer you to be honest." The simple Julia was delighted.

"Well, then, I'll be more honest. I agree with your father. Toby ought to be in the country."

"Why?"

Flitfoot took a lighter tone:

"Because there are fewer people to bite in the country, and the clothes they wear aren't so expensive."

Julia's answering smile was uncertain.

"Then you think he *is* dangerous?" She gazed up at him.

"I do."

"But yesterday you told father you thought he *wasn't* dangerous!"

"I was wrong to say that." Flitfoot leaned closer to the subdued girl.

"But I didn't know you then. I know you better now. Yesterday I was only lying to humour a pretty woman. Today -"

Julia glanced downwards.

"I can't let poor Toby go," she murmured.

Flitfoot leaned still closer.

"Miss Marsington," said he, quietly but terribly masterful. "Will you please look at me?"

Julia did not move.

"Please!" An immense force of will radiated from him. Slowly she raised her eyes to his.

"It may seem a little thing," he spoke solemnly. "But it's a big thing. You *can* let Toby go. And you will – for your own sake."

"Must I?" she breathed.

"You must."

"It's *you* who are ruthless!" she surrendered.

Flitfoot leaned back and laughed. His laugh was victoriously benignant, but it was also the laugh of one who has taken a great risk and escaped.

"Now will you forgive me for any frightful impertinence?" he said.

"I can only thank you," she replied submissively and sweetly, "for teaching me a lesson."

Sir Joshua came into the room, fussily as usual. He was followed by Toby, whose nose lifted itself suddenly into a questing mood.

"Sorry I'm late," said Sir Joshua, shaking hands with Flitfoot. "But I'm so busy. Really people have to consult me about everything." Sir Joshua felt a deep sympathy with himself.

Toby advanced towards Flitfoot, with a certain menace in his demeanour.

"Go to your basket, Toby," Julia ordered.

Toby ignored her.

"It will be all right," said Flitfoot quietly.

He fixed the dog with his eyes.

"Lie down!" said he to the dog.

Toby's eyes quailed. He retired to his basket.

"Quite simple," said Flitfoot to Julia, with a soothing smile.

Julia smiled in return. A certain genuine intimacy between them seemed to be established.

"Here's your tea, dad." Julia had poured out the tea. "And now poor Toby must have his biscuit. Oh! That waiter has forgotten it again. Really!"

"The usual thing," said Flitfoot quickly. "Service flat without the service. I made the manager change my floor-waiter the other day. I pay for service. If I don't get service, there's a clear breaking of contract. I threatened a writ. I had a new waiter in ten minutes."

"Yes," said Sir Joshua. "And I expect we've got your old one!"

"I'm sorry," said Flitfoot. "But do as I did and you'll soon have what you want."

"I will," said Sir Joshua stoutly. "Julia, ring the bell for the fellow."

"No," said Julia. "I'm tired of ringing for him. I have some of the biscuits in my room. I'll fetch one." She added as she left: "You needn't worry about Toby any more dad, I'm going to send him into the country. Mr. Flitfoot says you are quite right."

Said Sir Joshua, as soon as the two men were alone:

"You must be a magician. *I* couldn't persuade her to send the infernal animal away."

"Indeed!" said Flitfoot softly. "I found her quite amenable."

"She's the most amenable girl ever born - except where that dog's concerned." Sir Joshua rose and walked about the room, then added: "Are you as much of a magician with the income-tax authorities as you've shown yourself with Julia my daughter?"

"I'm not a magician. I only try to explain a case clearly."

"Anybody who can explain income-tax clearly is a magician. Listen. I'm a director of eight companies," said Sir Joshua importantly. "And chairman of four. Electricity supply,[1] as probably you know."

"Everybody knows," said Flitfoot.

"I was wondering whether you'd care to prepare the income-tax returns for all my companies. You might save us a lot of money."

Flitfoot answered modestly:

"But you don't know anything about me."

"I know more about you than I did yesterday." Sir Joshua grinned with amiable condescension.

"How?"

"Made enquiries. I don't mind telling you I was rather struck with you yesterday. Today I'm still more struck. The idea occurred to me that you might –" Sir Joshua waved a hand.

"You're very kind," said Flitfoot. "But I shouldn't like to take business away from another agent."

"You wouldn't. He's dead."

"Income-tax agents do die," said Flitfoot. "I suppose it's the wear and tear."

"What do you say to it?"

"Well," said Flitfoot, with studious negligence, "we might talk it over - one of these days."

"Tomorrow?"

"Not tomorrow. I shall have to be at Somerset House[2] and may be kept there," said Flitfoot blandly.

"Then the day after?"

"Sorry. I have to go away for a few days after that to the North."

"Say Thursday next week."

"Yes, with pleasure," Flitfoot accepted.

"Shall I come to your office? Yes, I'll take you out to lunch," Sir Joshua grandiosely offered.

"Very good of you, Sir Joshua! And I'm greatly flattered by this suggestion of yours," said Flitfoot, with softened glance. "Never so flattered in my life. I must tell you I've often watched your wonderful career with envy."

"Not at all wonderful," Sir Joshua protested unconvincingly. "I've only worked hard."

"It's not work. It's genius. Everyone knows you started with nothing."

"A fiver," Sir Joshua put in.

"Ah! That's £4.17.6 better than the traditional half-crown."

Sir Joshua laughed ponderously.

Flitfoot went on:

"And now you're the electric king of London! I say that's genius."

"So they call me the electric king of London? I never heard that before."

Sir Joshua's delight was open.

"*I*'ve heard it. The electric king of London! And a millionaire!"

"Yes, yes."

"A millionaire twice over perhaps?"

"No. Only once. I couldn't say my income is more than a thousand pounds a week. Still, that's not bad interest on a fiver, is it?"

"Ah, Sir Joshua. I said I envied you. And I do."

"You'll be a millionaire yourself one day, my boy."

"Never! That wants financial genius, but I'm a mere accountant." The bland insincerity of Flitfoot's humility was almost cruel.

"Well, well," Sir Joshua comforted him. "We all do what we can."

"Of course, after all," said Flitfoot suddenly, with a blazing glance, "I *might* be a millionaire."

Sir Joshua seemed startled, discomposed, almost frightened.

"No!" said Flitfoot. "That's only a dream."

Julia returned with the biscuit, and went straight to Toby's basket.

Flitfoot rose and approached her.

"Miss Marsington," said he appealingly. "Don't give it him."

"Why not?"

"A dog ought to have no scraps and only one meal a day."

"Toby has three meals a day."

"That's two too many."

"But he always has three."

"That's cruelty to animals."

"Mr. Flitfoot!"

"Yes, I mean it."

"But now I've offered him the biscuit and he's seen it –"

"Splendid for his character for him to *see* it - and then to lose it," said Flitfoot.

"Why?"

"He will learn the greatest of all lessons - that a dog's life can't be all biscuit."

"But the poor darling will be so disappointed."

Flitfoot's voice changed swiftly to the apologetic:

"I beg your pardon, Miss Marsington. Please forgive me. I've no right –" At the same time his gaze burnt into her.

"I give in," said Julia, with a yielding, ingratiating smile.

And she put the biscuit on the tea-table.

"Flitfoot!" Sir Joshua exclaimed. "I must have some lessons from you."

Mr. Flitfoot diffidently deprecated the remark. Both father and daughter being decent, stupid persons, were completely unaware that they had been witnessing a brilliant display of acting by Mr. Flitfoot.

Julia went and kissed her father.

CHAPTER VI

Thursday in the following week.

Flitfoot's private office.

Miss Sligo, absorbed in her life-work, was performing her everlasting role of confidential secretary to Mr. Flitfoot.

Said Miss Sligo:

"Sir Joshua Marsington has rung to say that unless he hears to the contrary he will call before lunch."

"He needn't hear to the contrary. Let me have all those particulars about the electric light companies."

"You have them." Miss Sligo pointed.

"Let Sir Joshua wait a few minutes when he arrives. He's only coming here to see what my offices are like. I shall get him as a client." Flitfoot laughed. "But I don't want him to think that the entire staff are tumbling over one another to kowtow to him. No need for a band of music to play him in. Tell them outside."

"Yes. Mr. Chail is here."

"He's in a hurry for his pickings. Exactly how much have I made out of those Tidal Power shares?"

"We bought 10,000 at £11 last week. We sold them this morning at a fraction over £14. Profit £30,000 clear after paying brokerage and so on."

"A bit more than £30,000 then, isn't it?"

"It's £52.10/- more."

"Send Chail in in five minutes."

Miss Sligo left the room.

Flitfoot began to study the documents concerning the electric light companies.

Then Mr. Chail entered, and Mr. Flitfoot received him as though waking up from a dream.

"Sit down, my excellent friend," said Flitfoot. "Well, I bought 2,000 Tidal Power shares at $11\frac{1}{4}$. Serious risk, of course, seeing I couldn't have paid for them. However, it was all right. I sold at $13\frac{1}{4}$. You'll say I sold too soon, and I did. But in this share gambling it's always a good rule to sell too soon. I've cleared £4,000. It isn't much. But I'd sooner anyday make £4,000 than be run down by a motor-bus, wouldn't you?" Flitfoot did not conceal his high spirits. "Have a cigar." He reached for a cigar-box.

"Thank you," said Mr. Chail sadly. "But I couldn't face a cigar this morning."

"Come. Cheer up. You've covered yourself with glory as a prophet. But I must say it was rather risky for you to come here. I thought it was understood you only saw me in the strict privacy of my flat."

"That doesn't matter now. I've got the sack, Mr. Flitfoot."

Flitfoot laughed.

"What are you laughing at, Mr. Flitfoot?"

"Oh nothing. I only thought how amusing it is that I should get £4,000 and you should get the sack. I suppose you turned up drunk or something of the sort."

"No. They suspected me of giving away private information. No proofs. Only suspicion."

"And when they cross-examined you, you weren't very convincing, I expect."

"Perhaps I wasn't. So out I had to walk."

"Ah well!" said Flitfoot comfortingly. "You'll find another situation."

"How can I find another situation without a reference? They won't give me a reference," Chail whimpered.

"Ah, my excellent friend, you ought to have thought of that a bit earlier." Mr. Flitfoot lit a cigar. "You don't mind *me* smoking, do you?"

"I hope you'll be able to give me a job, sir."

"Are you mad? Or are you trying to be funny?"

"I'm not trying to be funny," said Chail very sincerely.

"You may not be trying, but you're succeeding. Me take a man who's been chucked for blabbing! A tippler! A fellow who loses his head when he's cross-examined. A man who on his own admission is untrustworthy and dishonest! A man who gives away – I should say *sells* – his employers' secrets! Besides, I have an absolute rule here against taking on anybody without a reference."

Mr. Chail , thunderstruck, said weakly:

"But I did it for you."

"You didn't. You did it for yourself. Hope of making a little by a piece of dishonesty."

"You shared in the dishonesty," said Mr. Chail, still weakly.

"Now listen to me. I'm the last person to hit a man when he's down. And so I won't be angry with you. But you know –you positively mustn't accuse *me* of dishonesty. You offered me information. Why should I refuse it? Do be logical."

"Then you don't feel you owe me anything?"

"But my excellent friend, of *course* I owe you something." Flitfoot swung round on his chair, opened the safe behind, and took out notes.

"Here's fifty pounds. I prefer to pay in cash than by cheque. Wouldn't do for us to be mixed up in any banking transaction with a man like you. Here you are. Wait! I'll make it guineas." Flitfoot made it guineas. "Take them with my blessing."

"Is this all? .... And you've cleared five thousand!" Chail protested.

Flitfoot protested:

"Do you want me to make you a present of the entire five thousand? Think of the risks I take. If the shares had fallen instead of rising I might have had to go bankrupt. You took no risk. You saw me for five minutes. You just opened your mouth, and fifty guineas falls into it. Rather handsome, I think. I wish *I* could make fifty guineas every time I opened my mouth."

Mr. Chail gathered up the notes.

The telephone gave a signal.

"In a moment," said Flitfoot into the receiver. And to Chail: "I hate to lose you, but people are waiting for me. Now take my advice. Be cheerful. It's the first duty of every Christian to be cheerful. If you aren't cheerful you never *will* get another job. Go right away and have a really good blow-out. Treat yourself to a bottle of champagne. Your pockets are full of money." Flitfoot shook Chail's hand, gaily patted him on the back, and persuaded him towards the door. Then suddenly serious: "And let all this be a lesson to you, my excellent friend."

In dismissing Mr. Chail, Mr. Flitfoot practiced the cheerfulness which he had preached.

Mr. Chail disappeared.

Miss Sligo entered.

"I say," said Flitfoot. "I've just made that man a present of fifty guineas. Foolish, of course; but somehow I can never resist an appeal, can I?"

"I don't know," replied Miss Sligo imperturbably.

"Have it entered under 'charity'," said Flitfoot.

"There's no column for charity in your cash-book," said Miss Sligo.

"Then start one."

CHAPTER VII

A few minutes later a young clerk had opened a door marked "Enquiries" in Flitfoot's offices.

The small Enquiries room was furnished with two desks, one wonderful, the other rather less wonderful; at the former sat an older clerk.

"He's here," said the young clerk, slipping very quickly into a chair behind the smaller desk.

Both clerks became extraordinarily industrious.

The next moment a moving mass of self-importance appeared through the doorway; Sir Joshua Marsington. The young clerk entirely ignored him. The older one looked up casually and returned to industry, as though the fate of empires depended upon a certain task being completed at a certain moment.

"Mr. Flitfoot in?" questioned Sir Joshua with an excusable slight impatience.

"What name, sir?" asked the clerk with a deference almost exaggerated.

"Sir Joshua Marsington."

The clerk neither went down on his knees, nor did he blench at the grandeur of the name. On the contrary his demeanour was specially designed to show that he had never heard the name before.

"Marsington, sir?"

"Marsington, Sir Joshua Marsington."

"Have you an appointment, sir?"

Sir Joshua had to control himself.

"Yes, *sir*."

The clerk glanced at a book and then glared at the clock.

"I see there is someone of the name Marsington down for

twelve o'clock, sir."

"Someone of the name of Marsington," Sir Joshua repeated to himself: and said aloud: "I am the 'someone named Marsington'. I'm a little late."

"Yes, sir," the clerk agreed, and, having used the telephone, he added, "In two minutes, Sir Joshua. Mr. Flitfoot is engaged at the moment. If you will be good enough to sit down."

Sir Joshua could complain of no lack of courtesy. Still, he was notably dissatisfied with his reception. He felt bound to parade his importance somehow, and so, instead of sitting down, he first strode to and fro in the room, then went out into the corridor and had glimpses of rooms as doors opened and shut.

In his private office, Flitfoot was demonstrating his own impatience to Miss Sligo.

"If the fellow thinks I'm going to wait here all day for him –"

Then he received the telephone warning of the clerk.

"The fellow's here." Miss Sligo made a move to depart, but Flitfoot stopped her with a gesture.

"Two minutes," said Flitfoot into the telephone. And to Miss Sligo: "Book a table for two at the Grand Babylon Grill. I'll just show his imperial highness what a lunch can be." He laughed. Very leisurely he lit a cigar, and then went out of his room to find and welcome the impatient Sir Joshua.

"My *dear* Sir Joshua," said he with urgent deference, drawing Julia's father out of the corridor into his room. "I can't tell you how sorry I am to have kept you waiting."

"Oh, not at all!" said Sir Joshua, rather resentfully.

"In a business like mine –"

"Quite," Sir Joshua agreed with reserve.

"You must come and lunch with me."

"But I asked you to lunch."

Flitfoot had forgotten this important fact.

"You did. And I've never forgotten it. But my chop-house is probably nearer than yours - the Grand Babylon. We can talk there. I expected you earlier."

"I really think," protested Sir Joshua, still affronted.

"I insist," said Flitfoot, with his characteristic sudden masterfulness.

"So do I," said Sir Joshua, glumly. "Why should you –"

"Sir Joshua," said Flitfoot, with a most winning smile. "May I be quite frank with you. I want you to lunch with me because I want to be seen at the Grand Babylon, where I'm very well-known, entertaining the electric king of London. It will do me no end of good. Do you despise me?"

Completely mollified, Sir Joshua raised his arms in surrender.

"If you think it will help you," he said grandly.

CHAPTER VIII

In the entrance hall of the Grill of the Grand Babylon Hotel,[1] Mr. Flitfoot, Sir Joshua being grandly present, indulged in one of his more innocent pleasures: namely, the enjoyment of the obsequiousness of the gorgeous attendants, which obsequiousness he always rewarded with somewhat extravagant tips. The cloakroom functionary never insulted him by giving him a ticket in exchange for his hat; according to the functionary his hat, though very like other hats, was a hat by itself, needing no label. The hat of Sir Joshua had a similar distinction when Flitfoot said:

"Sir Joshua is with me."

Flitfoot's entrance into the grill-room was perfectly satisfactory, proving as it did to Sir Joshua that Flitfoot was somebody, if not everybody, in the Grand Babylon Hotel.

"My table?" said he with assurance.

The second-in-command of the grill-room escorted the splendid pair to a table. Sir Joshua, who had never been in the place before, and was indeed not accustomed to the greater restaurants of London, felt scarcely at ease, until one of his City acquaintances recognised and nodded to him with respect; whereupon Sir Joshua spread out his feathers in plutocratic array.

"But this is not my table," said Flitfoot coldly to the head-waiter.

"No, Mr. Flitfoot. Not your usual table. That was taken before your secretary telephoned." The man's demeanour said: "Deign to forgive."

Flitfoot deigned, but with disapproval.

The head-waiter expressed gratitude with his spine.

A waiter arrived.

"You aren't my regular waiter," said Flitfoot, icily.

"No, sir."

"Send me my regular waiter, Giacomo - you know."

"Certainly, sir."

But instead of Giacomo the head-waiter appeared again.

"I want my regular waiter," said Flitfoot curtly.

"Extremely sorry, sir, but each waiter has a small group of tables and this table's not one of Giacomo's group."

"I see," said Flitfoot.

The head-waiter bowed and moved away.

"I say," Flitfoot recalled him.

"Yes, sir."

"Ask Mr. Cafferelli to come here."

"Certainly, sir."

Mr. Cafferelli was the manager of the grill-room, a potentate who held absolute sway over the entire staff, including all head-waiters.

Flitfoot felt that his prestige at the Grand Babylon was waning in the sight of Sir Joshua. The conversation between them lacked vivacity and continuity. Sir Joshua made a remark about the motor cars which, as could be seen through the vast plate-glass windows, were manoeuvring in the narrow space of the courtyard.

"I always have the same waiter when I come here, and I'll have him today," said Flitfoot, in a voice of steel, gazing at the window.

"Of course," Sir Joshua concurred.

"If you don't mind what measures I take to get him," Flitfoot added.

"Certainly not," said Sir Joshua. "These matters are always very interesting."

"This will be very interesting," said Flitfoot pointedly.

Mr. Cafferelli arrived, a potentate, but extremely placatory.

"I want Giacomo," said Flitfoot shortly.

"I'm very sorry, Mr. Flitfoot, but –"

Flitfoot picked up the heavy cruet from the table.

"You see this cruet, Caffarelli?" said he, with a glacial smile.

"Yes, sir."

"And you see that plate glass window?"

"Yes, sir."

"Well, if I can't have my old friend Giacomo to wait on us, at once, you will see something you've never seen before. You'll see the cruet go through the plate-glass window."

He swung the cruet. Occupants of neighbouring tables began to display curiosity about the strange phenomenon.

A pause. Sir Joshua wished he had been less ready to give Flitfoot *carte blanche* as to procedure. He found that the next minute might be interesting to excess.

Flitfoot and Caffarelli exchanged a long glance. Flitfoot had the sensation of a cord drawing back his right arm preparatory to the throw.

"I will send Giacomo at once," said Caffarelli, who foresaw a shindy and a scandal of the first order in his sacred grill-room.

"You're very kind," said Flitfoot, suddenly mild, urbane, smiling, attractive. "Thank you so much."

"But should you have thrown it?" asked Sir Joshua humorously.

"Naturally," laughed Flitfoot. "An empty threat is like a lath sword."

"Might have been awkward," said Sir Joshua.

"It would," Flitfoot laughed again, with exuberant cheerfulness.

Giacomo came. Flitfoot welcomed him gloriously. The repast was ordered; the usual waiter took instructions; and all went well.

But Sir Joshua had had a fright, which he could not wholly conceal.

The course of the meal flowed smoothly along. Nothing could have been more exquisitely cordial than Flitfoot's demeanour towards his cherished waiter.

Caffarelli, having paused at a table a few yards away, was moving slowly up the room. Flitfoot signalled to him, and he approached with his delicate Italian smile. Sir Joshua fell into qualms of apprehension.

"Caffarelli," said Flitfoot. "I really must congratulate you. That river-trout was marvellous."

Caffarelli bowed with unreserved gratification. His smile proved that in his vast experience of the world, he had learned how to wipe out from his mind all memory of threats and scandals.

"It was indeed," Sir Joshua concurred.

"Sir Joshua," said Flitfoot. "Let me introduce Mr. Caffarelli, the manager of the finest restaurant in the West End." Then to Caffarelli: "Sir Joshua Marsington."

"Ah!" said Caffarelli. "I am honoured. But I blush."

"You blush?" From Sir Joshua.

"We make our own electricity at the Grand Babylon."

The millionaire electric king was greatly flattered that this foreigner who passed his whole life in a restaurant should know who he was, and should reveal his knowledge with such quick ingenuity.

Caffarelli bowed again and departed.

"And now about *my* electricity?" said Sir Joshua. "We haven't begun yet, have we?"

"I was waiting for you," said Flitfoot.

"But I offered you the job of defending all my companies against the income-tax brigands last week. You didn't accept. You said you wanted to talk it over."

"Do you know why I said that?" Flitfoot demanded.

"No."

"Simply because I wished you to be quite sure that you really wanted to give me the job. I owe the pleasure of knowing you to a mere accident - call it a domestic accident. In such circumstances one sometimes acts on impulse."

"I never act on impulse," said Sir Joshua importantly.

"Generous impulse, I meant," said Flitfoot.

Sir Joshua shook his head, still more importantly, playing the role of electric king.

"Then on full reflection you *do* seriously ask me to take on the job?"

"I do."

Flitfoot's face flowered into a dazzling smile as he said: "Then need I say that I gratefully accept – and with enthusiasm? This is the greatest honour of all my career."

With a magnificent wave of the hand Sir Joshua pooh-poohed an idea so exaggerated.

"Yes it is," Flitfoot insisted. "And I want to begin to study your figures at once."

"Of course you will have to know everything."

"Everything, naturally," said Flitfoot. "I will meet you at your office this afternoon." His face was lighted by anticipatory energy.

"Not this afternoon," Sir Joshua objected.

"Yes this afternoon."

"But it will take a long time," Sir Joshua objected.

"Let it take till midnight."

"But I have another important appointment," Sir Joshua objected.

"It cannot be as important as this one," said Flitfoot, gazing firmly at his guest. "Sir Joshua. I'm an accountant. But in my own way I'm an artist too. This work for your companies attracts me tremendously. I want to give you the very best service I'm capable of. And I want to begin *now*."

Sir Joshua once again felt the terrific dominancy of those eyes and that will-power. His desire was to be firm with Flitfoot. But he could not. The accountant's personality overcame him. Flitfoot fought, without a word, without a movement, and won.

"Very well," Sir Joshua yielded. "We'll go to my office straight from here."

"Splendid!" said Flitfoot, and his glance instantly softened.

Sir Joshua had further qualms. But he comforted himself with the thought that he was engaging for his companies the enthusiasm of an expert whom not even the mandarins of Somerset House could possibly defeat.

"And now tell me things," said Flitfoot, as the coffee was brought. "Anything, everything about your companies. Nothing like facts from the fountain-head."

Sir Joshua looked around cautiously and saw that the restaurant was nearly empty. He talked. He talked freely, grandly and at great length about his electric light companies and his own share in their activities.

Flitfoot seemed to listen with the ardour of a man who, having drunk nothing for three days, finds his thirsty lips indeed at the fountain-head.

"That's my own position in a nutshell," said Sir Joshua at the close of a protracted and grandiloquent discourse.

"You've made it wonderfully clear," said Flitfoot. "So clear that I've had an idea – But I won't go into that because you must have had the idea yourself, and if you haven't acted on it there must be strong practical reasons against it - reasons that in my ignorance I don't appreciate."

"Tell me your idea," Sir Joshua encouraged with majesty the speciously modest accountant.

"A combine! An electric light combine, to exploit the whole of London! You are chairman of four companies, you are a large shareholder in four others. There are only 15 companies supplying electricity to London."

"But I control a majority of shares in only two companies, and even those shares are not all my own," said Sir Joshua.

"Then buy more shares. Buy shares everywhere. You have immense capital resources. And if you got control of a dozen companies you could do what you liked with London. London! You have immense capital resources."

"Not immense enough for that job."

"You could borrow as much as you wanted from your bankers on the security of the shares you bought."

"Share-prices would go up, my friend."

"Share-prices wouldn't go up as much as the profits of a combine would go up. You would –" here Mr. Flitfoot told off item by item on his excited fingers:

" 1. Reduce overhead charges.

" 2. Buy all your commodities cheaper. Especially coal. You might own coal-mines.

" 3. Standardise voltages.

" 4. Deal more firmly with the men's unions.

" And 5 – most important – defy the consumer and stop the movement for lowering the price of current. The consumer is growing restive. The consumer is forgetting that his sole business, *as* consumer, is to put money into your pocket and look pleasant. One day the Government will be forced by public opinion to buy out all your private electricity companies.[2] Think of how a united combine could squeeze the government. And just as the business of the consumer is to pay, so it is the business of a government to be squeezed. Governments expect it. I believe they enjoy it."

Flitfoot laughed like a gleeful boy, and went on to paint

for Sir Joshua a thrilling vision of what an electricity combine would mean. "Power-stations one after another[3] all in and round the vast city, chained together by one supreme power. All their dynamos whirring night and day in colossal palaces of industry to a single turn. Millions of wires carrying light to hundreds of thousands of buildings large and small. Yes, – even to the mansions of ministers and princes. Thousands of workmen, foremen, clerks, managers, subject to one sole authority, receiving wages from one sole source. Innumerable consumers receiving innumerable demand-notes, and grumbling, grumbling, grumbling, and paying, paying, paying; and all the money going by all sorts of devious routes into the pockets of one man, who sat in state at the summit of the entire structure – Sir Joshua Marsington."

The vision was almost blinding.

Flitfoot said: "Already you are called the electric king of London. But with a combine you would be far more than a king. You would be an emperor - emperor of the illuminations of the biggest city in the world. London is waiting to be sacked. What's the good of London if it can't be sacked?"

He laughed again, joyously, merrily, gleefully.

Then he stopped. And the Grand Babylon grill-room became a mere grill-room once more.

Sir Joshua was blinking under the tremendous brilliance of the vision.

"Shall we go?" Flitfoot suggested.

He did not ask for the bill. It was ready but he waved away Giacomo who was advancing with it.

They went out of the restaurant, now completely empty save for Giacomo and a few other waiters. As they went out, Flitfoot distributed fantastic tips; and the pair were ushered forth into the street with delighted subservient smiles such as only money can buy.

CHAPTER IX

Flitfoot's private office. A fortnight later. 6.30 p.m.

Miss Sligo entered to her employer with a pile of letters for signature.

"Come along, Miss Sligo," said Flitfoot impatiently as she shut the door.

"I'm coming," said Miss Sligo, and walked with her usual deliberation.

"What time is my appointment with that American person?"

"Seven thirty."

"I thought it was eight."

"Seven thirty. The Majestic." [1]

"Then I'm in a hurry. Have to change. You'd better sign those letters for me."

"Yes."

"Get my hat, etc. You won't be kept very late, will you?"

"Yes."

"Why?"

"Forgery always takes time. Thirty-seven forgeries."

"Oh nonsense!"

"And I have to transcribe nearly fifty pages of shorthand notes."

"You're overworked?"

"No."

"Of course all this new electric business means extra work for you."

"It does."

"By the way, seen your Bagdad café friend lately?"

"Who's that?"

"Sir Joshua's secretary. Mr. Meacham."

"Oh *him*! Sometimes."

"He working late too?"

"Sometimes."

"He ought to marry you." Flitfoot was preparing to depart.

"Not me!"

"Why not?"

"My rule is one bedroom one person."

"It's a sound rule. You might be hearing something interesting one of these nights."

"I might."

Mr. Flitfoot vanished in haste.

Miss Sligo sat down at his desk, spread out her feet, took one of her employer's cigars and began to smoke it. As she smoked she forged his signature to each of the letters.

CHAPTER X

Later in the evening Miss Sligo, having finished her forgeries and her transcriptions, and been to the post, walked along into a little side street near Amen Corner, and descended into the earth under an illuminated sign "Bagdad Café."

This place of refreshment, one of two or three which, for the convenience of late workers in the City, remained open until 11 p.m., was located in a cellar. A large cellar, a cushioned cellar, a picturesque cellar; but a cellar! Having no natural light, not a single window, it presented exactly the same aspect at 11 a.m. as at 11 p.m. For thirteen hours every day it offered to its habitués the discreet lure of shaded lamps and cosy corners; together with a choice of alimentary entertainment comprising such attractive items as mineral water, milk, cocoa, Bovril,[1] tea, coffee, chocolate, rolls, butter, jam, sandwiches, cakes, boiled eggs, and, as a special delicacy for gourmets, hot buttered toast. Also the further lure of the very natty and coquettish costume of its waitresses.

When Miss Sligo invaded the cellar, and took possession of a table in the furthest corner, there were only a handful of other customers and one waitress, who looked as tired as the customers. The customers were seated about, for at the Bagdad the convention was that everybody should sit as far as possible from everybody else.

The waitress received somewhat nonchalantly from that regular patron of the establishment, Miss Sligo, an order for tea and a scone. Miss Sligo opened a newspaper.

Then a very neat gentleman of about fifty years, in a silk hat, arrived, saw Miss Sligo, and raised the hat to her. She nodded in response and dropped her paper. There was ample room for two at Miss Sligo's table, but the gentleman took no advantage of this fact. He sat down at the next table. The pair did not even shake hands. Discretion was a cardinal virtue at the Bagdad.

"Good evening, Miss Smythe," the gentleman greeted the lady with a sigh. He was a sad-faced man, and apparently the weight of all the world was on his shoulders.

"Good evening, Mr. Meacham."

"Been kept late tonight," he suggested.

"Yes. You too?"

"Yes," said Mr. Meacham. "But if you'll excuse me asking, Miss Smythe, I thought all the manicurists in the City shut at 6 p.m.?"

"6.30," Miss Sligo corrected him. "Gives the dandy clerks a chance after their closing-hour."

"Well, let us say 6.30. I'm not inquisitive, but may I remark it's now after 10."

"It is," agreed Miss Sligo.

"Then?"

"I thought you weren't inquisitive. However, I'll explain to you. I often have private appointments at night. Tradesmen's wives and so on in Whitechapel and Aldgate.[2] Very saucy some of them are - about their hands, I mean."

"You don't say!"

"I do."

Miss Sligo seemed pleased. But Mr. Meacham did not know that her pleasure was due to her cleverness in inventing a good, glib lie in two seconds.

"And where do you keep your instrument case, Miss Smythe?"

"I thought you weren't inquisitive."

"Excuse me. I beg pardon."

"Granted. You'll be asking me what my real name is next," said Miss Sligo.

"Isn't Smythe your real name?"

"I thought you weren't inquisitive."

"I apologise."

"Granted."

"I see you're having tea and scone," said Mr. Meacham, in the way of small-talk.

"I am," said Miss Sligo as clearly as she could, her mouth being at that moment full of scone.

"I feel rather like a blow-out tonight. A bit tired."

"Hot buttered toast," said Miss Sligo.

"Now that's an idea."

"Lemon squash."

"Yes, yes. How nice it is to have things like that suggested to you. Almost makes me feel like a married man."

"I shouldn't feel like that if I were you," Miss Sligo advised him.

"No?"

"No. D'you know what I believe in?"

"I'm afraid I don't."

"One bedroom – one person. Safest in the end."

"Bit lonely," said Mr. Meacham.

"Not me," said Miss Sligo. "One's company. Two's a quarrel."

"You're a very remarkable woman," said Mr. Meacham.

"I am," said Miss Sligo.

Mr. Meacham gave his order to the nonchalant waitress.

"Well, Mr. Meacham," Miss Sligo resumed. "And how's the world using you?"

"Badly," was the reply. "I always have to bear the brunt when there's trouble at our head-office."

"Trouble?"

"Yes. Trouble between Sir Joshua and Mr. Forfar – you know the managing director of our West End Electric Supply

Company. I've told you about him before, haven't I?"

"You may have," Miss Sligo admitted.

"You see the old gentleman always takes Mr. Forfar's advice, Mr. Forfar being Scotch and hard-headed. Only now the old gentleman isn't taking Mr. Forfar's advice."

"Oh!"

"No! Sir Joshua's trying for what we call a combine, if you know what that is."

"I have a sort of notion of it."

"And he's buying shares at fancy prices in all the other electricity supply companies in London, and Mr. Forfar said to me, he said: 'Sir Joshua's gone loony,' he said."

"Oh!"

"And I'm what they call between the upper and nether millstones, if you understand me."

"Quite!" said Miss Sligo.

"Makes you feel a bit lonely and crushed" added Mr. Meacham. "It relieves me to tell you. And you being a manicurist, what does it matter in telling you?"

"Quite."

Mr. Meacham was served with his blow-out, and asked for salt to spice the meal.

"Read about that murder case?" Miss Sligo asked.

"Yes, I did read something about it."

"Fancy her doing him in in the back with scissors![3] That's what comes of not sticking to one bedroom one person. I must be getting away to mine."

"So soon?" Mr. Meacham sighed.

"It isn't soon. It's late. If I don't go now I shall have to strap-hang in all that theatre crowd."

Miss Sligo paid her bill and left the Bagdad. She walked quickly through deserted city streets to the Flitfoot offices, opened the portal with her latchkey, passed through the corridor, where open doors showed empty rooms, and entered Mr. Flitfoot's room, where she soon magnificently occupied Mr. Flitfoot's revolving arm-chair, and telephoned Mr. Flitfoot.

"Thought you'd like to know at once," said she, having talked at some length.

"*Fancy* prices, you say?" said Flitfoot from his flat in Belgravia.

"Yes. Fancy."

"He didn't say which companies?"

"He said all of them."

"I say, Sligo. I want you to be at the office early tomorrow. I've had a very nourishing dinner with Mr. Curtis, the American gent, and he's coming at 9.30 sharp tomorrow. I go into his British income. He's leaving for Paris at 11. Have everything in order before he arrives."

"Right" said Miss Sligo laconically.

She hung up the receiver, put one of Flitfoot's cigars into her handbag, and in five minutes was in a Tube train – nearly as empty as the Bagdad Café. Within the next half hour she was in her one-roomed lodging in a most respectable small villa at Ealing.[4] A very plain room, with a very narrow bed. The chief article in it seemed to be an alarm-clock. In no time at all she was wrapped up in a dressing-gown over her night dress. She set the alarm-clock. She got into bed. She lit the cigar and smoked and read a book entitled *The Wife-Slave*. When she had finished her cigar she blew out the candle. The clock showed a quarter to two. Next morning, as the alarm-clock showed seven, she woke up with a fearful start, stuck the clock under the mattress to stifle its noise, made her own breakfast, dressed while eating the same, and at five minutes to eight was back at the station, and in the Tube train again. The train was packed. She arrived at the scene of her day's work at 8.45.

The charwoman was just leaving.

"Ye look very nice and fresh, Miss," said the charwoman.

"I am," said Miss Sligo. "Have you dusted that clock today I told you about?"

CHAPTER XI

Mr. Flitfoot was not very long after Miss Sligo that morning; but he did not arrive before she had collated all the Curtiss documents for him from the various departments of the office. He glanced through them quickly.

"Everything appears to be in order," said he.

"Not *appears* in order," she replied. "*Is* in order."

Mr. Flitfoot opened his cigar cabinet.

"Someone appears to be pinching my cigars," said he.

"Not appears to be pinching them. *Is* pinching them," said she smiling.

"You've noticed it?"

"I have."

"Who can it be?"

"Even if I knew I shouldn't say. I never tell against the staff."

"What am I to do?"

"I was going to put this piece of paper inside the cabinet." Miss Sligo produced a typewritten sheet, which contained the following words:

"I have counted these cigars."

Mr. Flitfoot laughed as he lit a cigar.

"If you will initial it," she suggested.

Mr. Flitfoot initialled the paper and put it inside the cabinet.

"You are a genius, Sligo," said he.

"If you say it," said she.

At this point, the time being exactly 9.30, Mr. John Champ Curtiss, the American millionaire, was ushered into the room, and Miss Sligo left.

Mr. Curtiss was a fairly tall, very slim and clean-shaven

man, nearly bald. Such hair as he had was black. His face had the aspect of a Jesuit priest. He was smoking a cigar, and he offered a cigar to Flitfoot.

"Try mine. Specially made for me," said he.

Flitfoot abandoned his own cigar.

Mr. Curtiss had come in carrying a small object wrapped in two layers of paper. He unfolded the packet and put on the desk a Chinese vase.

"What about it?" said he. "It excited me greatly when I saw it in a window in St. James's Street[1] yesterday afternoon. The dealer opened his shop half an hour earlier for me this morning. He wanted 30,000 dollars for the thing. I gave him 25,000. Isn't it lovely?"

Flitfoot, who knew nothing of Chinese porcelain, produced an excellent imitation of artistic enthusiasm.

"I sort of have to carry it about with me," said Mr. Curtiss, "and look at it at frequent intervals. It will be the finest thing of its kind in America," he added.

"I'll wrap it up again now," he said. "Your clock right?"

"Naturally," said Flitfoot.

"I've thirty minutes then," said Mr. Curtiss. "I've got to see my wife at the front of the Grand Babylon before I get the train for Victoria. She wasn't awake when I left. Where are my documents?"

Flitfoot gave him the documents, which Mr. Curtiss examined in detail. The pair discussed them. Mr. Curtiss made notes. Said Mr. Curtiss:

"What you told me last night appears to be pretty accurate."

"Not *appears*," said Flitfoot, gazing at him. "*Is* accurate."

"You ought to be in New York, not London," said Mr. Curtiss.

Flitfoot laughed.

"I can pick up a living here. London will still struggle on pretty well, you'll find."

"I wonder how London does it," said Mr. Curtiss, "with those taxes. Sure, I've got a business here. I work hard at it when I'm in England. I employ over a thousand people. And about twenty-five per cent of my profits go to your brigand of a government."

"That's true," Flitfoot agreed. "But if you choose to run a very successful business, you must take the consequences. You made a profit of over £100,000 this last year on a big capital, and £25,000 of it goes to the Treasury. But if instead of running a business you bought £100,000 of somebody's shares and sold them for £200,000, as you might, gained a profit of £100,000 without any work and without giving employment to anyone, and the government wouldn't take a penny of your profit."

"And that's England."

"It is."

"You've got something on your mind, Mr. Flitfoot," said Mr. Curtiss suddenly.

"You're a thought reader."

"Yes, I make a living by reading other people's thoughts."

"Do you want a big thing?" asked Flitfoot with solemnity.

"Bigger the better," said Mr. Curtiss.

"It would need a lot of capital."

"The more the better."

"What limit?"

"No limit, within reason."

"What's 'reason'?"

"A hundred million dollars."

"And where should *I* come in?" asked Flitfoot.

"You've got some capital, I suppose?"

"Fifty thousand pounds - a quarter of a million dollars,"

said Flitfoot.

"That's more than I had at your age," said Mr. Curtiss. "In fact it's only within the last two years I've made a bit. Till then I couldn't honestly say I was worth more than five million dollars."

"A trifle," commented Flitfoot. "I ask you again. Where would I come in?"

"Look here," said Mr. Curtiss. "Look into my eyes. I'm straight. I've never gone back on a partner. And I've never spared an enemy. If I like your affair, I'll give you a quarter of the plunder. One quarter. And you can keep your quarter of a million dollars. I'll find all the capital. I'll write it."

"You needn't," said Flitfoot. "I'll tell you in two words. There's going to be an attempt to form a combine of all the electricity supply companies in London, which is a city of seven million people. This bit of news is absolutely secret. Nobody knows I've heard about it. You can fight the combine. If you acquire a majority in certain shares you'll win, and if you win you'll have three quarters of London in your pocket. I shall have the other quarter."

Mr. Curtiss smiled, and lit another cigar.

"Big possibilities," he murmured, impressed.

"Very big," said Flitfoot.

"We'll talk about this," said Mr. Curtiss. "I'm going to buy a Rembrandt at a sale in Paris tomorrow morning, and I promise you I shall startle the world. I meant to go on to Berlin. But I'll be back in London tomorrow night instead. We'll talk."

"Friend," said Flitfoot, "it'll mean a fight."

"I always fight to the death," said Mr. Curtiss. "And I'm still alive. It's the other fellows who are dead."

"We're a pair," said Flitfoot.

"I think we are," Mr. Curtiss agreed.

He looked at his watch, gathered up his Chinese vase, and

departed. Flitfoot did the arch-plutocrat the honour of conducting him to his car. As he was entering the car Mr. Curtiss let fall the vase on the pavement.

"Some people would call that an omen," said Mr. Curtiss.

"I simply don't believe in omens," said Flitfoot.

Then, staring at the packet on the pavement, he raised his head and laughed enormously.

"What are you laughing at?" Mr. Curtiss demanded.

"Well, it *is* rather a gorgeous joke, isn't it? You just paying 25,000 dollars for a bit of earthenware and then letting it smash itself to bits!"

"But do you realise that that was a most lovely thing?" demanded Mr. Curtiss, gravely. "And it's gone for ever?"

"There are millions of lovely things in the world," said Flitfoot.

"Some people might call you callous!" said Mr. Curtiss.

"Not at all," said Flitfoot. "But I can always bear other people's misfortunes cheerfully."

"However," said Mr. Curtiss, who had picked up and opened the packet, "by a miracle it isn't broken."

"I think I rather *do* believe in omens," said Flitfoot.

When he returned to his room he found an invitation to dinner in Julia's handwriting, for the next night at Sir Joshua's flat. The dinner was to be followed by a visit to the West End Electricity station or power-house.

CHAPTER XII

At the dinner the only other guest was Mr. Forfar, Sir Joshua's head man. Flitfoot was on Julia's right, Mr. Forfar on her left. Sir Joshua sat opposite his daughter, to whom, as the meal progressed, Mr. Forfar grew more and more attentive - though only sporadically attentive.

Mr. Forfar, as becomes an Aberdeen Scotsman, was obviously dour. Also he was unimaginative and well set in his opinions. Although only of about the same age as Flitfoot, who had already had the educative experience of several meetings with him on Sir Joshua's business, he looked older. He was thickset; his thin hair was graying; his hands were stubby. He seemed to make little effort to hide his opinion that Sir Joshua was a simpleton who would always need strong and sagacious guidance, nor his opinion that Flitfoot was a man to beware of. He never laughed; and Flitfoot's jolly demeanour awoke no sort of gay response in him.

The dinner was over. Mr. Forfar had begun to crack nuts in the intervals of sipping port. Sir Joshua joined him in the consumption of the port. Flitfoot drank little of anything, and no port.

Flitfoot produced from his pocket some papers containing figures. Such a gesture was always the signal for Julia to leave the table at her father's business dinners.

"We shall be going to the West End power-house in about three quarters of an hour, my child," said Sir Joshua.

"Couldn't I go with you," said Julia timidly.

"No, no. It's no place for a girl like you. You'd better go and see a picture.[1] Take your maid," said Sir Joshua.

Julia left the room. The two guests resumed their seats.

Flitfoot passed the papers across to Mr. Forfar, who

glanced at them with a certain negligence.

"I'll examine them tomorrow," said Mr. Forfar. "I may say I think your suggestions are pretty good. But I thought we were going to talk tonight about the governor's new scheme for an electrical combine."

"What scheme is that?" Flitfoot asked innocently.

"But wasn't it you that started it?"

"Oh *that*!" said Flitfoot, with a smile of indifference. "I believe I did just mention it to Sir Joshua. The idea occurred to me - just as an idea. I never dreamed that it would be taken seriously."

Mr. Forfar replied harshly:

"Well, it *is* being taken seriously."

"I've been putting out one or two feelers – that's all," Sir Joshua rather timidly interjected at this point.

Flitfoot smiled meditatively to himself, reflecting that neither Sir Joshua nor Mr. Forfar was aware of the private information reaching him through Miss Sligo. Evidently also Sir Joshua had come near to lying when he spoke of 'putting out one or two feelers'. Actually buying shares right and left at fancy prices could not be fairly described as putting out one or two feelers.

"I'd like to discuss it, if Sir Joshua has no objection," said Forfar.

"Discuss it with whom?" Flitfoot blandly asked.

"You."

"It has nothing to do with me," said Flitfoot. "One has an idea in conversation. One mentions it. That's all. My job is income-tax returns; it isn't combines. I don't know anything about combines."

Mr. Forfar challenged him:

"Then you won't tell me again what you told Sir Joshua that day at lunch?"

"Of course I will," said Flitfoot.

They talked, argued, drank, struck matches, knocked over a wine-glass or so, dropped their serviettes, and picked them up again. Cigar smoke thickened the air.

"The scheme of course needs enterprise and imagination," said Flitfoot. "Without those qualities –"

"Of course," Sir Joshua agreed proudly. "That's what I keep saying to Forfar."

"Without these qualities," Flitfoot proceeded, "I see no hope for the scheme."

"Neither do I," said Mr. Forfar grimly.

"*With* these qualities –" said Flitfoot.

"Nor with them either!" said Mr. Forfar curtly.

"As I was saying," said Flitfoot, "with these qualities I am convinced that the scheme would succeed, and be highly profitable."

"Well, I'm not convinced," said Mr. Forfar, still more curtly.

The two opponents faced one another.

"You may be right," said Flitfoot softly, diplomatically, and yet contemptuously. "You're more likely to be right than I am. I'm not an expert in business. I'm only an expert in accounts. Anyhow it doesn't matter. You are advising Sir Joshua against the scheme, and no doubt that will settle its hash." He glanced at Sir Joshua, as if daring him to defy his Mr. Forfar.

"*I* decide these things, don't I, Forfar?" said Sir Joshua, with an uneasy grin.

"You do, governor," Mr. Forfar admitted.

"I listen to all advice. Then I come to a decision."

"You *have* come to a decision, governor," said Mr. Forfar.

"Well," said Sir Joshua, "I have. Flitfoot's arguments seem to me to be unanswerable. I have decided to go on with the scheme for a combine."

"I won't answer for the consequences," said Mr. Forfar with extraordinary energy, banging the table. And with a glance at Flitfoot:

"I consider the whole idea most mischievous. Mischievous!"

Flitfoot walked quietly out of the room, smiling.

"My dear Forfar," Sir Joshua protested majestically, "why be so violent? Moreover you've hurt Flitfoot's feelings."

"I haven't, governor. He has mine."

The two continued to argue.

CHAPTER XIII

When Mr. Flitfoot entered the drawing-room, where Julia sat alone, he was wiping his brow.

"Bit hot in there," he said. "No need of a fire in any room where Mr. Forfar is arguing. May I sit here?"

Julia smiled, and he sank into a chair.

"I've heard many arguments in that room," said Julia.

"It's a shut door, but Mr. Forfar's arguments would come through any door," said Flitfoot.

"Father has the greatest confidence in him, but sometimes father gets an idea into his head, and not even Mr. Forfar can move him."

"This girl isn't so stupid as I fancied she was," Flitfoot reflected. And aloud: "That's what's happened. But won't you be late for your cinema?"

"I'm not going."

"It must be rather lonely for you without Toby," said Flitfoot.

"How nice of you to say that!" said Julia, touched.

"Well, come along with us and see the works."

Julia shook her head. "No! Father doesn't like me to mix myself up in business things."

"This isn't business."

"For father it's business."

"I think I could persuade him to let you go with us."

"It's sweet of you, Mr. Flitfoot," said Julia. "But you don't know father."

"Well then. *I* shan't go to the works either. There's no reason at all for me to go.... I say, Miss Julia, let me take you to the cinema."

"Dad wouldn't like it if I dragged you away from him."

"Please leave it to me?" asked Flitfoot quietly in a low tone - for the door was opening.

Julia had just time to give an excited half-frightened nod.

"Mr. Flitfoot," said Sir Joshua. "We'll be off. Forfar is putting his coat on."

"I don't think I'll come," said Flitfoot.

"Why not?" Sir Joshua gave faint signs of being huffed.

"Forfar wouldn't care for it. He's annoyed with me."

"Nonsense, my dear Flitfoot. That's only his Scotch way. Besides, Forfar doesn't happen to be God Almighty. *I*'ve asked you to come, and I want you to come. You'll find it all very interesting."

"I'm sure I should," said Flitfoot. "But the fact is I've asked Miss Julia to let me take her to the cinema."

Sir Joshua, somewhat overcome by the intertwining complications of domestic life and business life, suddenly saw the shortest way to peace and quiet.

"After all, you'd better come with us, Julia," said he, and moved away.

"Didn't I tell you I could persuade him?" Flitfoot murmured to her.

Julia felt that Flitfoot and herself were conspirators together and the feeling was very precious to her.

"I'll put on my new furs," she said, filled with pride and delight by the sudden turn of events.

"Don't be half an hour over it," Sir Joshua warned her.

Mr. Forfar, overcoated and hat in hand, came into the room. But he grimly ignored Flitfoot.

CHAPTER XIV

The party of four went off to the Power house in two cars, Sir Joshua's and Mr. Flitfoot's.

"I want to talk to you, Forfar," said Sir Joshua.

"Then shall I take Miss Julia?" Flitfoot suggested instantly.

Sir Joshua had no alternative but to agree:

"Please do."

Flitfoot's car left first. He was a man who demanded not only safety, but speed, from his chauffeur, and the second car was not seen again during the journey.

"I expect your father thought it wouldn't be a bad thing to separate me and Mr. Forfar for a bit," said Flitfoot. "And I'm not sorry. Are you, Miss Julia?"

"Why should I be?" said Julia, with a charming, candid, trusting smile, which had a considerable effect on Mr. Flitfoot.

"What's your view of Mr. Forfar?" he asked.

"I believe he's very good at his job."

"No, but I mean really. Do let's be frank. It's so much better for being frank. Do you like him?"

Flitfoot gazed at the young girl. He was enjoying her presence in the swift car. Under the influence of her smile his original estimate of her was still further changing. Stupid? Yes, perhaps she was slightly stupid. But she had a most endearing personality. Hence she could not be wholly stupid, because no girl could be wholly stupid who had an endearing personality.

"Now tell me?" he insisted. "Do you like him?"

"No," Julia answered briefly and simply.

Flitfoot was delighted by her honest simplicity. He thought:

"We are getting positively intimate. She must like me, and trust me too or she'd never have answered like that."

And when the car stopped at the dark entrance to the hundred generating meters, a tiny incident occurred which somehow increased his admiration for her. A wandering mongrel came up on a mission of enquiry out of one of the mean streets nearby, stood in front of Julia and hesitatingly wagged his tail. Julia stooped and absently patted the animal's head; and his tail began to wag furiously. It was nothing, nothing at all. But Flitfoot was impressed. This curious instinct for human character, and so on and so on. All nonsense of course, he argued masculinely, still he was impressed, despite his scorn for the race of dogs, and his detestation of at least one specimen of the race.

"We'd better wait for father," said Julia. "He'll want to show us himself."

They gazed up at the frontage of the enormous building which was dark save for the glow of a few lofty windows. An immense vibration filled the air. Through one window, lower down, they could see the huge, slow revolutions of machinery.

"You're a mover," said Sir Joshua to Flitfoot when the second car arrived.

"I am," Flitfoot admitted.

They all went in, the doorkeeper receiving Sir Joshua and Mr. Forfar with ceremonious honours.

"Why! It's bigger than a cathedral," said Julia to Flitfoot. "I never knew there could be any place as big as this in the world."

She added, after a moment:

"It frightens me."

Flitfoot saw that it did frighten her. And she might well be excused for being frightened. The colossal interior, very long and very wide, and in addition very high – higher than any cathedral, seemed empty. Yet the gigantic machinery was stealthily moving in it, and some dozens of human beings, workmen, dwarfed by their surroundings and the size of pigmies, were walking about in it.

Flitfoot himself, who had never in his life before seen a London generating station, was taken aback by the mere dimensions of the affair.

He said to Julia:

"This is the reality behind the share-certificates of the West End Electric Light Company."

Julia looked at him, only half comprehending.

But now Sir Joshua took charge of the party. He had the air of having himself created the whole organism. He was more than the chairman of the Company. He was majestic; he was god-like. And he explained what all that terrific, reverberating, deafening machinery was doing at that moment: lighting whole streets, whole boroughs, lighting thousands of houses, heating hundreds of rooms and offices, moving many scores of lifts up and down, moving hundreds of tramcars along their lines. (He would have liked to be able to say that the organism was also moving crowded trains in underground tubes; but he could not.)

Here was indeed the intimidating reality of electricity.

Julia said again to Flitfoot - they were following behind Sir Joshua, Mr. Forfar and the manager of the station, rather in the style of tourists following an official guide in a cathedral:

"It really does frighten me."

"Nothing at all to be frightened about," Flitfoot soothed the girl gently.

Sir Joshua beckoned Flitfoot to approach and listen more closely to his august remarks. They were all now near to the main mass of the shaking, thunderous machinery.

A moment later Flitfoot, out of the tail of his eye, saw the mongrel dog running to and fro somewhat wildly. The animal was probably just as frightened as Julia herself.

The next moment, still nearer to the machinery, he saw a

workman make a wild kick at the dog.

And then there was a faintly-heard jarring noise; then a complete silence far more startling than the thunder of gigantic dynamos; then darkness, in which could be heard the brief maddened yelping of the dog.

The darkness, however, was not as complete as the silence had been. Here and there in the apparently limitless interior burned a few lamps maintained for just such an emergency, independently of the chief supply of current.

The dog, scared into insanity by his formidable surroundings and by the kick of the employee, who knew the danger of dogs in the proximity of machinery, had plunged violently, blindly, against moving metal, disarranged some trifle of steel, and so brought about a breakdown.

Figures ran darkly to and fro.

Flitfoot gazed around in the gloom for Julia. She was not to be descried. She had mysteriously vanished from the scene. He ran here and there, more interested in her welfare than he had ever been in the welfare of anybody except himself.

At length he descried her lying flat on the concrete floor in a distant corner. But Mr. Forfar had found her first. He ran. Mr. Forfar was lifting her head and shoulders from the ground.

"Let her lie flat, you idiot," Flitfoot cried angrily. "She's only fainted. If you lift her up how can the blood get back to her head? Drop her, you – d – d fool!"

By force he pulled Mr. Forfar away. The Scotsman had momentarily lost his senses.

The two men glared at one another over the prostate body of the unconscious girl. A workman came up and flashed an electric torch on the two.

"I will look after her," said Mr. Forfar savagely.

"Not while I'm here!" said Flitfoot savagely.

The wandering beam of the torch fell on the dog's corpse

a few yards away. Julia, seeing the dog, had hastened after it and while doing so had fainted.

"What is it?" demanded an agitated voice – Sir Joshua's. "Julia!"

"Nothing," said Flitfoot calmly. "She's only fainted. She'll come to in a moment. She's not hurt. A bit frightened, that's all."

"I'll look after her, Sir Joshua," said Mr. Forfar, officiously.

"As managing director of this place," said Sir Joshua pompously, imperiously, "you've got something else to do. Come along to Morrison at once. This is a serious breakdown. Flitfoot, will you get her out and take her home."

Sir Joshua, deeply enjoying the exercise of his own authority, and at the moment less concerned for his daughter than for the good name of his generating station, walked smartly away, and Mr. Forfar had to obey.

Julia became conscious.

Flitfoot picked her up, balanced her on his shoulder, and carried her off like a victorious warrior in the sack of a city. He cared nothing for the breakdown. He was absorbed in his burden, whose weight was delicious to him. He had a feeling of happiness such as he had never had in his life.

"Light me out of this place," he ordered the torch bearer.

In the open air, Julia revived completely. Flitfoot had installed her in his car. Crowds were collecting in front of the vast building now as dark as the pit.

"Drive right away!" he said curtly to the chauffeur. "Drive through them. They'll scatter quick enough."

And the crowd did scatter.

"How do you feel now?" he questioned Julia softly.

"I'm quite all right," she answered. "How silly of me to faint!"

"Not at all. It was very natural you should faint."

"But –"

"Don't worry," he interrupted her imperatively. "It's nothing. Your father asked me to take you home. There's only been a little breakdown. Breakdowns do happen sometimes. This is one. They'll soon have the thing working again. Nobody was hurt - except a dog, and that was the dog's own fault."

"But–"

"There is no 'but'," said Flitfoot. "As you see, I'm rather glad it happened."

"Glad? Why?"

"Because it's given me a chance to look after you."

Julia made no reply.

"A good thing I was there!" Flitfoot added. "That blundering fellow Forfar was doing everything wrong for you. You'd think a grown man would know how to treat a woman who's fainted. But he didn't."

"Did he touch me?" asked Julia.

"He did," said Flitfoot.

It seemed to Flitfoot that she shuddered. His delight increased.

In the streets everything seemed to be as usual. Street lamps blazed; shops were fully lighted; motor buses and cars moved normally. There were no tram lines.

"Now you're crying," said Flitfoot with tenderness.

"I was thinking of that poor dog.... My fault. If I hadn't stroked him he wouldn't have followed us in."

"Yes," said Flitfoot. "That was your fault - the fault of your absurdly kind heart. But I won't let you blame yourself."

Suddenly the automobile ran into another borough, a region of darkness, one of the districts whose electricity was supplied by the West End generating station. There were trams here; but in the unlit gloom every tram stood still and black, immovable. The street lamps were extinguished. Candles burned feebly in shops and in windows. Within some of the larger buildings lifts, with people imprisoned therein, had halted motionless between two floors. The sole illumination of the street came from the head lights of automobiles, and from the improvised torches of joyous boys. Traffic crawled. At arterial crossroads half-dazed policemen tried to put order into the confused medley of innumerable groping vehicles. The effect was tremendously sinister. The district might have been stricken by some offended god.

And then, after a passage of time apparently endless, light was re-born everywhere in a flash. The street-lamps glittered; the shops blazed with incandescent bulbs. The lifts moved. The trams resumed their cruises. The citizens shouted "Hurrah!" It was all magical!

The breakdown had been repaired.

"How thrilling!" Julia exclaimed with childlike relief.

And Flitfoot himself was thrilled by the spectacle.

"It's rightly called a *power*-station!" said he, with emotion.

Julia glanced up at him admiringly, feeling towards him as she might have felt towards a pet.

Flitfoot wanted the ride to last for ever.

CHAPTER XV

Flitfoot got out of the descending lift at Belmont Mansions and saw Mr. Forfar standing opposite to him in the entrance-hall, separated from him only by the steel grille of the lift.

He slowly slid back the grille.

"Where's Miss Julia?" Mr. Forfar demanded.

"I have safely delivered her into the hands of her maid," said Flitfoot. "And I hope that she is now in bed. She is quite well. Where is Sir Joshua?"

"He will be here shortly," said Mr. Forfar.

"I congratulate you on your speed in repairing the breakdown," said Flitfoot.

Mr. Forfar retorted grimly:

"I wish I could congratulate you on your language to me in the generating-station."

"You ought to congratulate me," said Flitfoot calmly. "It was excellent language in the circumstances."

"Some of the workmen must have heard it," said Mr. Forfar.

"I wish all London could have heard it," said Flitfoot.

"I shall be even with you one day," said Mr. Forfar.

"That remains to be seen," said Flitfoot.

The pair were as furiously jealous of each other as two dogs.

"I was just going out to tell Sir Joshua about his daughter. I needn't now. And as Miss Julia is perfectly recovered, you needn't go up. Good night."

Flitfoot closed the grille, pressed a button, and ascended out of sight, leaving Mr. Forfar in the hall.

CHAPTER XVI

One day Sir Joshua Marsington was shown into the manager's room of the City branch of his Bank with far more ceremony than had marked his entry into the offices of his income-tax agent Mr. Flitfoot.

The manager of the City branch of the British Standard Bank had all the characteristics of his calling and of his post: a non-committal face, a neat suit, a black necktie, and the consciousness of the power behind him of one of the Big Five banks.[1] He employed two kinds of demeanour, one demeanour for customers who had money to lend and the other for customers who wanted to borrow money. On this occasion, as on all previous similar occasions, it was the first kind of demeanour that he displayed to Sir Joshua Marsington. He knew a good deal about Sir Joshua's financial situation, and he had reason to be very well satisfied with all that he knew. He gave Sir Joshua the easiest chair; also a cigarette; and then, not without the deference due to a certified millionaire, he sat down himself.

"I don't want to borrow–" Sir Joshua began.

The bank-manager laughed at the mere conception of Sir Joshua as a borrower.

"But one of these days I *might* want to borrow. I don't say that I shall; but I may." The tone of the last sentence showed some pomposity.

The face of the bank-manager changed; not a lot, but it changed; and Sir Joshua noticed the change.

"I'm investing rather heavily in the shares of electric supply companies throughout London," said Sir Joshua, with an air as casual as he could command. "This of course is confidential. I needn't go into my reasons. I will only say that

I am extending my activities in the supply of electricity to London. There will be developments which I wish to be in a position to take advantage of. Hence I may need financial help."

"Quite," said the bank-manager. "Then no doubt, seeing that your realisable resources are large, your proposed new investments will be very large too."

"They will," said Sir Joshua proudly. "My operations will be on an immense scale."

"Of course," said the manager, "the general opinion is that electricity supply shares already stand in the market at their full value."

"The general opinion is wrong," said Sir Joshua.

"You ought to know better than anyone," said the manager politely.

"I do," said Sir Joshua.

"Your operations have already begun?" said the manager. The remark was in the form of a question; but it was really a statement, for having had notice of Sir Joshua's visit, the manager had examined somewhat closely all Sir Joshua's recent transactions with the Bank.

"They have," said Sir Joshua.

"Just so."

"I might want half a million sooner or later," said Sir Joshua.

"Large figures," commented the manager.

"Your daughter has a very considerable fortune," said the manager, who was thoroughly familiar with the affairs of the Marsington family. "Could you not use some of her capital. You would find that way cheaper, I think."

"No," said Sir Joshua firmly. "My daughter's money is my daughter's. She had it from her mother. I handled my late wife's affairs for some years – of course with her full approval

– and I took some risks with them. Everything turned out all right, as you know."

"Quite," said the manager.

"But I will never take such risks again – with money not my own."

"Quite," said the manager.

"The security which I shall offer will be ample."

"I am sure of it," said the manager.

"All I have come for today is to warn you that I may need loans, and to get your assurance that the loans will be forthcoming."

"I am sure there will be no difficulty," said the manager. "None whatever. But I must tell you that, though I am the head of the Bank's largest branch, even I have no power to advance any money beyond a certain sum. I may say in confidence that every loan of £20,000 or more has to be authorised by the General Manager of the Bank in person."

"Then you will kindly inform him," said Sir Joshua grandiosely. "And let me know the result tomorrow."

"But you say you won't want help just at present, and may not want it at all."

"Exactly," said Sir Joshua. "But I wish to know where I stand. I do nothing in the dark. It is understood? Tomorrow."

"It is understood," said the manager.

Sir Joshua rose to go.

Sir Joshua's income per week was about as large as the manager's income per annum. Nevertheless the manager now shook hands with the millionaire as an equal – perhaps indeed as rather more than an equal. The manager had control of something that Sir Joshua might want.

And Sir Joshua did not feel quite as much at ease as he seemed.

CHAPTER XVII

[The following scene might perhaps run in and out simultaneously with the previous scene.][1]

Mr. John Champ Curtiss was shown in to Flitfoot's private office the next morning.

After greetings, the American said gaily to the Englishman:

"Seen this morning's papers?"

For answer Flitfoot picked up a newspaper from his desk, and pointed to headlines:

Sale of a Rembrandt portrait
for 2,500,000 francs

Record for a Paris auction sale
John C. Curtiss's triumph[2]

"Well," said Mr. Curtiss. "It was some fun." He went on without a pause: "Now about that electricity supply notion of yours. I've got most of the figures out of the County Council handbook." Which handbook he pulled out of his pocket, at the same time as he pulled out a cigar.

"Here!" said Flitfoot. "You'll have one of my cigars this morning."

"Not on your life!" said Mr. Curtiss.

"I think you will," said Flitfoot. "There are times when even the buyer of a hundred-thousand-pound picture does as I ask."

The pair fronted one another.

"I step down," said Mr. Curtiss, after a pause.

Flitfoot opened the special cigar-box. He took out the paper which Miss Sligo had prepared several days previously, and read first the original words: "I have counted these cigars". A type-written line had been added underneath: "The hell you have!"

"What's the matter?" asked Mr. Curtiss.

Flitfoot laughed aloud and showed the paper, curtly explaining the circumstances.

"Why, Henry!" said Mr. Curtiss. "The secret of England's greatness is in that last line. The man that wrote it will succeed."

"Not if I can stop him," said Flitfoot, as hard as flint.

They smiled.

"To return," said Flitfoot casually. "I interrupted you, John. Now I'll tell you some more about that proposed combine."

"You needn't," said Mr. Curtiss. He added pointedly: "It may be better for you if you're in a position to say that you haven't told me anything."

"Not a bit!" Flitfoot contradicted, but not convincingly.

"Well, you never know. Anyhow I've got all the news I want. There are only 15 electrical companies supplying London. The total capital of all of them is only £23,000,000. With half that sum at the most I can swoop the lot. I will swoop the lot. Yerkes[3] came over from New York to London and took hold of London's underground railways. I'll take hold of London's electricity supply. Yerkes is dead. I'm not."

"You mean that?"

"I mean everything I say - when I'm talking to a man like you, Henry. And let me tell you, my son, that the electricity business hasn't begun yet in London. Not begun. Instead of selling 500 million units as they do now, we'll sell 2,000 million units. We'll create a demand. We'll sell the juice at a loss if necessary till the demand is there. When I've done with the thing every house in London will be cooking by electricity, warming itself by electricity, living by electricity. And after that - well, you'll see. There isn't a Britisher in this island that realises the possible profits from cheap electricity. Not one, except that fellow H. G. Wells."[4]

"And how shall you set about getting hold of shares?"

"You leave that to me. I've got my agents, and I can trust them. Nobody will know that I'm on top till I *am* on top. Say, this cigar is what I call a cigar. When it comes to the point you have all the best things in London, including cigars."

"Glad you think so."

"I think so. Goodbye. I've got a date with my wife." Mr. Curtiss halted on his way out. "Say, sonny. D'ye know what I like about you?"

"My cigars."

"Something else. I like you not saying a word to me about your share of the swag in this electricity circus."

"What you told me last time you were here was good enough for me."

"Shake!" said Mr. Curtiss and, having shaken, proceeded to the door.

"I say, John," Flitfoot stopped him. "You know you'll be up against a tough proposition. You've got a serious rival, and he's at work already."

"So much the worse for him," said Mr. Curtiss gaily. "If me being on top means him going under, he'll go under. You can bet your shirt on that."

Flitfoot smiled serenely.

CHAPTER XVIII

In his flat late one Saturday night Henry Flitfoot was preparing to go to bed when there was a ring at his door. He put on his dressing-gown and opened the door and saw Miss Sligo, who entered, shut the door and stood with her back to it. She looked very tired.

"News," said she. "If you go down to Oakfield Castle tomorrow afternoon, you will find Miss Julia alone there after all."

"But you said to me that Sir Joshua was going down today for the weekend."

"Yes. But he's decided to leave again early tomorrow morning, on some other business in the country. Seems he's always changing his plans just now."

"You're quite sure."

"I'm quite sure. I've been told so."

"Meacham."

"Yes."

"Then I'll call there after the lunch at Andover. But I must have the dope."

"What dope?"

"You know. I gave it you to keep."

"Oh, *that*! It's in your safe at the office."

"I'm leaving at eight in the morning. Let me have it here by then. I'm off to bed now."

"I can't say the same," said Miss Sligo, glancing at the clock, which showed two minutes to midnight. With a grimace, but without a word, she opened the door to leave.

"Goodnight, Sligo," said Flitfoot.

"It won't be very good," said Miss Sligo, and banged the door.

She went back first to the city, then to Ealing and to bed, into which she installed herself at 1.30 a.m.

The next morning Flitfoot stepped into his car as the clock struck eight.

"Seen Miss Sligo?" he asked the chauffeur.

"No, sir."

"Wait."

Flitfoot settled himself in the car.

Miss Sligo appeared and handed to her employer the small box which weeks earlier he had taken from the mantelpiece in Sir Joshua's drawing-room.

"Thanks. You're a minute late," said he.

"Indeed!" said she. "But there's one thing – I'm alive."

"I hope you'll have a pleasant Sunday," said Flitfoot laughing. "What are you going to do?"

"I'm thinking of taking a look at my bed for a change," said she.

"You should go and visit your friends," said he. "Liven you up!"

"I've only got one friend," said she. "My bed. The poor thing must have been missing me dreadfully these last weeks."

CHAPTER XIX

In the afternoon Flitfoot's car passed up the drive leading through Oakfield Park to Oakfield Castle, and halted at the august portals of that magnificent residence whose antique exterior and interiors had been so often portrayed in the weekly illustrated papers. This was Flitfoot's first sight of the impressive spectacle.

A footman opened the portals.

"Sir Joshua at home?"

"No, sir."

"Miss Julia at home?"

"I don't think so, sir."

"Now listen, my friend," said Flitfoot. "Don't tire yourself with thinking. I'll think for you, and I'll think Miss Julia *is* at home. Take my card."

Flitfoot strode into the vast entrance-hall. The footman vanished. In a moment the butler himself appeared, a superb specimen.

"Miss Julia will see you, sir."

"How's Toby?" Flitfoot enquired, with a wise smile, which the butler appreciated.

"Not at his best, sir. A protracted indisposition. Miss Julia is very anxious about him."

"Dogs are mortal," said Flitfoot, going into an empty drawing-room.

Julia, who had been wandering rather disconsolate about the house, came in, obviously excited and pleased.

"I was in the neighbourhood," Flitfoot explained. "And I thought I might ask for a cup of tea. I hear your father is away."

"He'll be back tonight. You must stay and see him," said

Julia, and to the butler: "Tea, please."

"You must be a bit lonely here, all by yourself."

"I have Toby," said Julia. "I really came down here to look after the poor old thing."

"Basket's empty I see," said Flitfoot.

"Ah! The tea will bring him."

The tea did bring Toby. He strolled wearily into the drawing-room in the wake of the butler and two footmen. The sight of Flitfoot excited the dog as much as it had excited his mistress. But apparently, it did not please him. Without the slightest delay he became young and sprightly again, and sprang at Flitfoot's wrist.

"He's bitten you!" exclaimed Julia, aghast.

"No, no!" said Flitfoot.

"Down! You naughty, naughty dog! Go to your basket."

Julia spoke in a tone of command which surprised Flitfoot. The dog's instant obedience also surprised him.

"I can't tell you how sorry I am!" said Julia. "He's so old and so unwell. Father said I should have to get rid of him. But I can't bring myself to do it. I can't. I can't.... Now I'm spilling the tea."

"Not at all," Flitfoot reassured her. "Toby's all right. I quite see how it is. He's never forgotten the kick my friend gave him that afternoon in my flat. He associates me with the kick. Very natural on his part, *I* think."

Said Julia: "You've always been so kind about Toby! I wish father was half as kind."

"You're too nice about me, and not nice enough about the author of your being."

Julia sprang up.

"You're bleeding!" she cried. "He *did* bite you!"

"Did he?" Flitfoot laughed. "So he did. It's nothing."

But there was indeed blood on his wrist. Flitfoot wiped

off the stain with his handkerchief. The stain reappeared.

Julia almost hysterically rang the bell and told the butler to bring in warm water, bandages and a sponge.

"Toby has bitten Mr. Flitfoot," said she.

"Yes, miss," said the butler. And it was as if he said: "Nothing that that dog did would surprise me."

Equipped with the surgical appliances, Julia began to tend Flitfoot's wrist.

Flitfoot said suddenly: "No! I can't bear it."

"Is it so painful?" Tears stood in Julia's eyes.

"Not at all painful. But please let me do it myself. I can't bear you so near me."

"Why not? Am I so clumsy?"

"No. You aren't clumsy. But you're something else – to me at any rate. When you touch me I'm too thrilled. And I've no right to be thrilled."

Flitfoot meant what he said. The girl's touch did thrill him. He vividly remembered the contact of her body as he carried her on his shoulder out of the generating station. Ever since that night she had dwelt in his mind, and now his mind was full to bursting with the thought of her.

Said Julia smiling, happily enchanted: "Nonsense! There! How's that?" She had finished the dressing.

"I'm glad I was bitten," said Flitfoot. "And yet I'm sorry. Because there's no denying I'm in great danger."

"But Toby isn't mad!"

"No. But I'm mad. And you're in danger too. Please may I have some more tea?"

He had more tea.

"You're sad here," said Flitfoot gently. And to himself: "She's just as mad about me as I am about her." A new and strange secret joy overcame him.

"No," said Julia. "I'm only upset about this bite."

"Yes, you are sad here" Flitfoot insisted, in a tone of intimacy. "If you hadn't been in a sad mood you wouldn't be crying about such a little thing as a bite."

"I'm not crying."

"Yes, you are."

"Well," said Julia, "Yes. I *am* sad."

"Why? Tell me."

"I'd tell you anything," said Julia. "I'm sad because father wants to sell this house. Three years ago mother died here and father hates it for that. He doesn't want any country house, he says. Prefers to be always in London. You see, he's so absorbed in his business. More so than ever, lately."

"Oh! More so than ever?"

"Yes. And because mother died here I want to keep the house. Every room in it reminds me of her, and I love to be reminded of her."

Said Flitfoot: "I can understand your father. And I can understand you."

"Of course you can. But nobody else could. I know how sympathetic you are. I never met anyone like you."

"And I never met anyone like you," said Flitfoot, in emotional accents which disconcerted Julia.

"Would you care to see the gardens?" she suggested, with that tact and instinct for self-preservation which every girl possesses, however inexperienced she may be.

She left the room to find a hat. As soon as she was gone Flitfoot withdrew the pill from the little box, pushed it into a piece of cake, then he hesitated a moment, but invisible irresistible cords seemed to be pulling at his right hand, and he threw the cake to Toby, who caught it with an unnerving aim of the mouth. In the tenth of a second the cake had vanished. Flitfoot went to get his hat in the hall, where Julia met him. Toby followed close at her heels.

"He loves to walk with me," she said. "He ought to be punished. I'm fearfully angry with him – but he's such a friend I *can't* be angry with him. You naughty, naughty dog!" she turned to the animal. "Don't you see the bandage on Mr. Flitfoot's wrist? That's *you*!"

They walked in the gardens. After a few moments, while still in sight of the front entrance, Toby lay down, unnoticed by his friend and his enemy, and did not move again.

"But where's Toby?" asked Julia, looking round. "Toby! Toby!"

No answer.

She returned, Flitfoot following her, and found Toby dead in the path. Julia maintained her composure admirably. The butler, whose business it was to know everything, arrived.

"A peaceful end!" said Flitfoot.

And he gave the butler a look of fellow-feeling such as no gentleman ought to give a servant. The butler similarly misbehaved himself.

"Wouldn't you have a post mortem?" Flitfoot suggested. "The poor thing may have been poisoned."

"Poisoned!" cried Julia. "Impossible. All the servants adored Toby, didn't they Simmons?"

"Certainly, miss," answered the butler, imperturbably, and glanced again with understanding at Flitfoot.

"Dear Mr. Flitfoot, will you see that he is buried at once. You know the place, Simmons?"

"Yes, miss."

"I couldn't bear to see it myself. But perhaps the servants would like to," said Julia.

"I'm sure they would, miss," said the butler.

With that Julia burst into tears and ran weeping into the house.

A gardener was summoned from his Sunday rest to act as

gravedigger. A number of servants appeared. The burial was accomplished. As the last earth was being thrown into the hole at the bottom of which lay the deceased Toby, Flitfoot said suddenly – somehow he could not help saying it:

"In a way it was I who killed the poor fellow. He bit me. He died."

The servants discreetly laughed.

There was a scream. Julia, drawn in spite of herself to the funeral, was standing imperceived a few yards away. She had heard and she had seen.

Again she ran off.

Flitfoot, disturbed by the consequences of his impish rashness, went quietly after her and overtook her in the drawing-room, where she sat on a sofa in tears.

"I can't bear to see you crying," said Flitfoot.

"Why did you say that?" she protested. "Why did you say such a thing?"

"Forgive me," Flitfoot said softly. "I only wanted to be cheerful. I always do want to be cheerful. I believe in cheerfulness. I'm frightfully sorry. Forgive me. Say you forgive me!"

He sat down beside her and took her hand.

"I've no friend in the world now," she moaned.

Said Flitfoot in a furious tone:

"You must not say that – to me. *I* am your friend, and you know it."

"Yes," she murmured. "Oh! Your bandage is loose again."

She put the bandage right.

"Julia," said Flitfoot. "Excuse me. I must say it. Don't listen to me, but I must say it. I'm wildly in love with you. I'm always thinking of you. I can't sleep for thinking of you. You're the sweetest girl–"

He was indeed wildly in love with her.

"But we've only–" Julia began.

He interrupted her.

"I know. I know. We've only seen each other seven times .... seven is a mystic number. I know I'm in too much of a hurry. But I can't help it. I'm in love." Then masterfully: "Julia. You've got to be my wife. You know you have." Then in still another tone: "No, no! I'm not good enough for you. You won't be my wife. So I must leave you. That's my only chance. I must never see you again. Goodbye."

He half rose.

"Don't go," she whispered, looking up at him.

They kissed.

He was intensely happy. The angelic sweetness of Julia's face; her exquisite acquiescence; the thought of existence with this loving, submissive creature – these ideas intoxicated him. He said: "Do you know what I should have done if you had turned from me, my darling."

"No," she said.

"Neither do I. But it would have been something desperate. Darling, I shall confess to you. You shall know the worst about me. I'm very masterful. I can be hard and cruel. If I want a thing I *must* have it. I *must* use every power to get what I want. I can't help it."

Said Julia:

"I like you to be masterful. And you shall have everything you want."

They talked.

Then he said:

"And you shall go on living here. If necessary, I'll buy this place from your father. You shall be the queen of it .... and I say, my sweet Julia. Let all this be our secret for a while. Don't let us say a word about our being engaged. It wouldn't quite do for us to seem precipitate, would it?"

She nodded, submissive and enchanted.

"Our lovely, heavenly secret!" she murmured. "Of course father may object - when he knows. He's rather queer sometimes."

"I always get what I want, dearest," said Flitfoot confidently.

He bent over her, dominating. She looked up at him, dominated, acquiescent, anxious and pleased to be ruled. Both of them were full of happy emotion.

Suddenly Flitfoot moved away from the sofa and rang the bell.

"You allow me?" he said; then added: "I was only thinking that that peer of the realm, your butler, might be coming in at any moment and disturb us to take away these tea things. Let's get that over."

CHAPTER XX

The butler answered the bell, but Sir Joshua himself was the first person to enter the drawing-room. The second person to enter was a rather obese gentleman, unknown to Flitfoot. The third person was the butler, who with the aid of two footmen accomplished the arduous task of removing the tea things.

Meanwhile:

"My dear fellow," Sir Joshua greeted Flitfoot. "I'm delighted to see you."

Flitfoot replied:

"I understood that you were here for the weekend, and as I was in the neighbourhood I ventured to call. Miss Julia has been very hospitable. Indeed I never before received such hospitality in any house."

"You'll stay for dinner," said Sir Joshua. "No ceremony. Parre," he turned to the stranger. "Let me introduce Mr. Flitfoot, our income-tax wizard."

And to Flitfoot again: "Lord Parre – you know – chairman of the Brampton and South Kensington Electrical Supply Company. He will dine with us too."

Lord Parre had turned to salute Julia, who took his hand with the utmost marked distant coldness. The next moment she astonishingly said:

"Daddy, I'm not very well. If you'll excuse me I'll go and lie down."

She shook hands with Flitfoot and left the room.

Flitfoot thought:

"What the old man said is true. She likes precious few men. In fact only one, and – I'm the man –"

Constraint fell on the three males in a manner quite dramatic.

"Er – may I use your telephone, Marsington?" asked Lord Parre, and he too left the room. He seemed to know the house. Lord Parre said into the telephone:

"Call me up in a quarter of an hour, and say I'm urgently wanted at home. I couldn't stand a dinner here."

In a quarter of an hour Lord Parre, having made his excuses, effusive but still constrained, had gone, and Flitfoot and Sir Joshua were left alone. Sir Joshua's demeanour was extremely forlorn. Pompousness and majesty had vanished from his countenance.

"What's the matter with my girl?" he asked, trying to be intimate - he always had a difficulty in achieving the note of intimacy. "Has she said anything to you, Flitfoot?"

"It's very simple," said Flitfoot easily, and related the history of Toby's sudden decease, showing his bandaged wrist.

"Well," said Sir Joshua. "I'm sorry about your hand; otherwise this is the best piece of news I've heard for a long time. The fact is Julia's been wasting on that dog what she ought to have been giving to - some *man*. She wants a man – and that's all there is to it."

"Probably," said Flitfoot, with due cautious respect.

"But she's so damned difficult to please," said Sir Joshua.

"Is she?"

"I don't mind telling you – I thought she might like Lord Parre. Landowner. Money. Very decent. Friend of mine. In our line of business. Everything all right. But no! You saw how she received him!"

"Yes," said Flitfoot. "Thermometer fell right down to zero, didn't it?"

Sir Joshua laughed awkwardly.

"I'm very fond of my girl, and she's very fond of me. But she's making mincemeat of my existence. And that's flat."

The butler entered.

"What time would you like dinner, Sir Joshua?"

"The sooner the better," said Sir Joshua. Mr. Flitfoot is staying."

"I think I'd better go," said Flitfoot, modestly.

"I think not," said Sir Joshua with authority.

Mr. Flitfoot bowed with becoming gratitude.

"Miss Julia asked me to say that she will dine upstairs in her room," said the butler.

"There you are!" said Sir Joshua, after the man had left. "That's only because she thinks Parre is here. Well, let her dine upstairs! Come, my boy, I'll show you the house."

Later, when the dinner was over and Sir Joshua was engaged upon the port he began to talk again. The sherry and champagne which had preceded the port were assisting his tongue.

"In confidence," said he, "I've been nearly all day with Parre trying to get a price for his holding in the Brampton and South Kensington Company. It's considerable. He won't take less than £3.10/- a share. It's too high."

Flitfoot agreed in the privacy of his hand; but he answered "I'm not sure. The more I think it over, the more I'm convinced that even at £3.10/- the shares will prove to be cheap in the end."

"That's your opinion?" said Sir Joshua, startled.

"It is."

"Oh, well! Perhaps I might close, then. But if there could have been anything between Julia and Parre, I believe I could have got him down to £2.15/-. Everything would have been different. Sort of family affair then. In fact it would have been ideal. However, if she won't, she won't. And there's nothing more to be said."

"I suppose Miss Julia is very much attached to this house?" said Flitfoot.

"Why do you suppose that?"

"She gave me a hint – nothing; still a hint."

"I'd like to sell it," said Sir Joshua.

"How much?" Flitfoot asked.

"I got it cheap. No demand for large houses these days. I gave £30,000 for it."

"I'll give you £30,000 for it," said Flitfoot.

"You!"

"Yes. I've made money. And I shall make a lot more. Of course I might mortgage the place at first." Flitfoot spoke firmly.

"The deuce!" exclaimed Sir Joshua. "Well, as I say, I'd sell like a shot. But Julia simply won't let me. She'd buy it herself, but of course I couldn't take *her* money for it. Moreover I should still have her on my hands."

"Then Miss Julia has her own fortune?"

"She has. And a big one. And she'll have the absolutely free handling of it too in about a fortnight's time, when she's twenty-one."

"She's not twenty-one yet!"

"No."

"I'm sorry she's so rich," said Flitfoot. "That puts a different complexion on the matter."

"What matter?"

"Sir Joshua," said Flitfoot grandly. "You've spoken freely and I appreciate the compliment. May I speak freely? I must. I like your daughter."

"Do you mean –"

"I do. But I'm not after money. And I won't let you think I'm after money."

"But, my dear fellow, she won't look at any man."

"Perhaps not. Probably not. But have I your permission to try? I know it's like my cheek."

"You don't need my permission," said Sir Joshua.

"I know that," said Flitfoot pointedly. "But I'd like it. Do you give it me? Yes, or no?"

After a pause Sir Joshua said:

"Yes. But you won't succeed."

Upstairs Julia was typing a letter: "My darling Harry, But I must call you Harry, of course ...."

"I daresay not. But if I do, I'll buy the place from you. Your daughter could stay, and she'd be off your hands, as you say." There was the ring of victory in Flitfoot's voice.

"You'd have a handful, my lad."

"I like handfuls," said Flitfoot, who knew that he would not. He laughed.

"Go ahead then," said Sir Joshua. "All this is quite different from anything I intended. But go ahead."

"Sir Joshua," said Flitfoot, "I needn't tell you, because you know. I have never in my life felt so honoured."

Sir Joshua was his pompous, majestic self again.

CHAPTER XXI

Sir Joshua was rung up at his flat one afternoon at tea-time about a month later by a clerk, who said to him:

"The Bank manager has sent a note asking you instead of calling on him tomorrow at 3 p.m. as arranged, to call at the head-office of the Bank at noon, when the General Manager will see you himself."

"Very well," replied Sir Joshua to the clerk laconically, and to himself, after hanging up the receiver, he said, with false cheerfulness: "All the same to me!"

The truth was that he felt considerably disturbed. He had asked for a further loan from the British Standard Bank and his original appointment with the manager of the City branch was to discuss and settle the matter. Now apparently the affair had been taken out of the hands of the City branch of the Head-Office. The great General Manager was deigning to interest himself personally in the question of the loan. A compliment of course, to the financial importance in the City of the equally great Sir Joshua. But sinister! Sinister. The Bank could not conceivably refuse the loan, having regard to the security offered. And yet.... and yet.... Sir Joshua became jaunty, which with him was a sign that he did not feel jaunty. He slept ill.

The new premises of the head-office of the British Standard Bank were reputed to be the most magnificent premises in the city. In the first marble hall Sir Joshua was a mere human being. In the second marble hall Sir Joshua was a mere human being. At the inner office for enquiries he developed into somebody of a certain consequence. A liveried attendant took charge of him and led him through a marble corridor to a room gilded with the terrible words: "General Manager".

The attendant knocked respectfully at the door, opened it,

named a name, and the next moment Sir Joshua was shaking hands with the legendary General Manager whose long speeches every year were said to influence financial opinion throughout the world: – and then he became Sir Joshua Marsington himself, the electric king of London.

Four gentlemen stood round a table:- the General Manager, the two assistant managers - viceroys in the presence of their supreme sovereign - and a superior and very shiny sort of clerk with a file of papers in front of him. Sir Joshua made the fifth at the board. Everybody sat down, the General Manager first.

"We are just a little concerned about the further loan which you are asking for, Sir Joshua," said the General Manager. "Naturally it is our business, as well as our duty, as a Bank, to assist the development of industry by supplying capital – upon adequate security. But we should like to satisfy ourselves about the objects which you have in view–"

"I shall be perfectly frank," replied Sir Joshua grandly. "You know all about me. I am increasing my holdings in various Electric Supply Companies, and I want more money to pay for more shares."

"Quite. But let us come to details. For instance, we deduce from the records of our City Branch that you have paid Lord Parre for a large block of Brampton and South Kensington shares at the rate of £3.10/- a share. We think the price rather excessive. Of course the price is our affair only insofar as it concerns the value of the security which you offer us. I do not say that the security – is not ample – at present."

"The value of all London electric shares recently created by one of my companies, the West End, are at a premium of 10/-."

"Just so! Prices are going up. But are values going up? That is the important point. Are prices going up because there is an unusual demand for electric shares generally and is not that demand chiefly from yourself?"

"It may be so," said Sir Joshua stoutly.

But he had secret qualms. Never before had he listened to such plain questions about his activities. And he had to remember that the questioner was the representative of the biggest private financial institution in Great Britain - and one of the biggest in the world.

"No doubt," proceeded the General Manager, "your object in these dealings is to obtain control of the various companies, in fact, to obtain what would be practically a monopoly of the electricity supply."

"I don't say that," said Sir Joshua with assured modesty. "All I say is that I believe very strongly in the future of electricity in London, and I want to take advantage of the general position."

"You have recently been selling a lot of other securities, some of them gilt-edged?"

"Yes. For this very purpose."

"So that your available resources of liquid or semi-liquid capital are not so large as they were?"

"Perhaps not," Sir Joshua admitted, feeling more like a prisoner in the dock than the millionaire king of London electricity.

"There are rumours that someone, or several people, are competing with you in the market for electric shares," said the General Manager.

Sir Joshua was thunderstruck.

"It's the first I've heard of such a thing," said he, truthfully. "And I don't believe a word of it." This latter statement was possibly less truthful.

"I only said 'rumours'," the General Manager soothed the Bank's important customer.

Then the shiny clerk was called upon for a number of

details, which he gave with miraculous speed and precision. Sir Joshua finished his explanatory comments.

"Of course," said Sir Joshua audaciously. "If you don't care for the security, I can get what I need elsewhere. I don't want to urge you unduly - or at all."

"Of course! Of course!" the General Manager smoothly concurred. "We should like to oblige you–"

"I don't want to be 'obliged'," Sir Joshua pompously interrupted. "I want merely a business transaction." And as he spoke he wondered whether he was not taking too high a hand.

"Of course! Of course!" the General Manager repeated. "But you are an old customer, a valued customer. And it is in our own interest to continue to deal with you – if we possibly can. Now you have very kindly given us all the information we asked for, would you mind waiting a few minutes while we – er – confer?"

"With pleasure," said Sir Joshua.

And the shiny clerk conducted him into a small room adjoining the august council-chamber.

Sir Joshua was now considerably alarmed. He had said that he could get the accommodation elsewhere. But where? The 'Big Five' banks were all as thick as thieves together – they *were* thieves together (said Sir Joshua to himself unjustly) – and word would be passed from one to another. The 'Big Five' did steal one another's business, when they could, but only on terms of safety. And what was this rumour about a rival buying against him in the market? Absurd! And yet.... Had his tone been rather too audacious? The terrible last phrase of the General Manager echoed in his ears. "Continue to deal with you – *if we can*."

The clock in the room was going; Sir Joshua could see the pendulum swinging; but the fingers seemed to his impatience not to move.

At length the door was opened by the shiny clerk.

Sir Joshua's ageing legs literally did tremble as he re-entered the council-chamber. The moment was the most poignant, the most frightful, of his whole life. He felt as though he was awaiting the verdict of a jury: guilty or not guilty.

The General Manager smiled.

"I am glad to say," he began – "I am glad to say that after having gone further into the matter we feel justified in providing the accommodation which you asked for on the security you offer."

"Thanks," said Sir Joshua curtly.

"*But* –" the General Manager added, "naturally the period of the loan must depend on the courses of the share-market."

"Naturally," said Sir Joshua gravely. "But I've no fear on that score. None."

The two assistant managers and the shiny clerk left the room. The General Manager grew much more affable.

"Forgive me for suggesting," said the General Manager with extraordinary affability, and yet somehow with a warning sternness, "that, considering the nature of your operations you may possibly have been moving just a *little* too quickly - too precipitately. Forgive me. I speak as a friend."

"Quite! Quite!" said Sir Joshua coldly. He felt affronted. The infernal impudence of this salaried official trying to teach a lesson to *him*, Sir Joshua!

For all his bravado, as he quitted the vast building, Sir Joshua felt acutely that he had been through a harrowing experience. He had fought, and he had won. Everything was all right. But supposing the Bank had refused to accommodate him....?

Back in his office, Sir Joshua, as it were instinctively, glanced at the mirror – to assure himself that his hair had not grown whiter in an hour!

CHAPTER XXII

Sir Joshua entered his flat that afternoon in a mood at once superficially triumphant and secretly apprehensive. He found Julia and Flitfoot sitting together at the remains of a plenteous tea.

"You *are* late, father," Julia greeted him, rather nervously.

"Business," said Sir Joshua. "Important business. Very important. Hello, Flitfoot!"

"I'll order some fresh tea, daddy," said Julia.

"Don't," said Sir Joshua. "I've asked for a whisky and soda. I don't feel like tea."

At that moment the flunkey arrived with a tray.

Sir Joshua mixed himself a drink, and swallowed it quickly. Then he mixed a second drink.

"You aren't worried, are you, dad?" Julia asked anxiously.

"I've had a heavy day. But I'm not a bit worried, my girl."

"Then if I may say so, sir," said Flitfoot brightly, "you ought to be worried."

"Why?"

"There's been a burglary in this flat of yours. And the most valuable thing in it has been stolen. Julia said *I* was to tell you. Well, I've told you."

"What?" exclaimed Sir Joshua.

"Yes, sir. I am the burglar, and your daughter is the stolen property. But she has consented to be stolen."

"You aren't angry, are you, dad?" said Julia.

She went up to her father and kissed him.

"There!" said Sir Joshua. "You've made me spill my whisky."

"I must say you don't seem very surprised, dad," Julia remarked.

Flitfoot winked privately at his future father-in-law, unseen by his future wife. He then winked privately at his future wife, unseen by his future father-in-law.

"And now, sir," said Flitfoot. "I wish to buy Oakfields from you. You don't want it. Julia does. I should like to give it to her for a wedding-present.

"Harry!" exclaimed Julia. "Why shouldn't *I* buy it? I've got plenty of money for a trifle like that."

"No!" said Flitfoot firmly. "My wife must live in *my* house. That's an ultimatum."

Julia kissed him.

"Dad!" said Julia suddenly. "You *are* worried. I know you are. I've noticed it for weeks."

"If you mean I'm worried about money – *me*! –" said Sir Joshua, expansively, "you're a silly little fool, my girl, and no fit wife for a clever man."

"Oh! I'm so glad!" breathed Julia.

Sir Joshua turned to Flitfoot.

"I had a bit of a tussle with the Bank today," he remarked easily, as one confident man of affairs to another. "But I soon brought them to their senses. When I pointed out to them how those new West End shares had risen to such a high premium, all in a week or two, they began to change their tune, I can tell you. And I said a few other things too. I didn't mince matters."

"I understand" said Flitfoot. "You got all you wanted."

"I certainly did," said Sir Joshua.

"Of course you did," Flitfoot agreed, cheerfully and respectfully and reassuringly.

Julia, however, seemed a little troubled. She did not understand business, but she understood the look on a man's face, and there was something in her father's face that puzzled her.

"I should just like to say this, sir," Flitfoot added with the utmost benevolence. "However wealthy a man may be, when his operations are on as big a scale as yours are, it won't harm him to know that two friends are behind him. And I want to tell you that at all times in the future, all our combined resources –" Flitfoot took Julia's hand – "are absolutely at your disposal."

"You're very good with your *combined resources*" answered Sir Joshua rather resentfully. "But I shan't need them. Just let me inform you once for all that my position is as secure as ever it was, and that's saying something." He paused impressively with his mouth open. Then finished, "You'll excuse me now, children. I've got one or two little things to attend to."

He went off into his own room. But, seated in the chair at his desk there, he attended to nothing, little or big. He just sat and stared at the wall-paper. "'Moving a little too quickly,' am I?" he reflected, repeating the phrase of the General Manager.

"Damn the fellow!"

"Darling, Harry!" said Julia, in the drawing-room, putting her arms round Flitfoot's neck. "How splendid you are! You said just what I wanted you to say. Of course with you to look after him the old dad is bound to be all right."

"I think so!" said Flitfoot, with perfect assurance. And he kissed her passionately, for he was deeply in love.

CHAPTER XXIII

The balcony of a suite of rooms in the Hotel Splendide on the Riviera. The façade of the great building stretched upwards to flagstaffs from which waved French, English and American flags, and stretched downwards to a piazza and waving palms, hill-scenery, magnificent and picturesque on either side. Pale blue sky without a cloud. Deep blue sea with scarcely a ripple. Brilliant and intense morning sunshine.

The doors of a French window opened from one of the rooms and out on to the balcony stepped Julia, the young wife, smiling to herself in all the felicity of a perfect honeymoon. She was clad in a gay negligée for the breakfast of which the chief necessaries were already laid out on a table between two armchairs. Julia leaned on her half-bare arms on the balcony and gazed enraptured at the vast and lovely spectacle of nature in front of her. She kept glancing round to the same door from which she had just emerged. Then a waiter appeared with a tray of hot coffee and hot milk. Then Henry Flitfoot appeared. He was half dressed for walking, except that he wore a dressing-jacket instead of his lounge-suit. And Flitfoot too was smiling in the same felicity as Julia.

"Harry, tell me again you are happy."

"I was never so happy."

Julia said ecstatically: "I am so happy that I can scarcely bear it."

She kissed him with passion.

"But people will see us, my darling!" he protested.

"I don't care who sees us," Julia answered sternly. "I'm brazen."

Sitting down to the light meal, they both laughed joyously. The honeymoon was a tremendous success, for

Flitfoot as much as for Julia. Indeed Henry Flitfoot was as profoundly in love with Julia as Julia with Henry Flitfoot. He had not expected such bliss.

Julia tasted his coffee, to be sure it was hot enough, sweet enough, and had the right proportion of milk. She added another lump of sugar.

"I know your taste better than you do yourself," said she. Their fingers touched affectionately across the table. An ideal had been attained. Everything was forgotten save love and bliss.

"What shall we do today, darling?" asked Henry.

"It simply doesn't matter, darling," Julia replied.

As Henry looked at his wife, drowning her in his gaze, he reflected: "How could I ever have thought that this enchanting creature was stupid and uninteresting? I would have married her if she'd been a pauper instead of a very rich woman - and glad to!"

Then a page appeared at the open window, with a rather large bundle of letters held together with string.

"My mail!" exclaimed Flitfoot, in his eyes the glint of a new interest.

And into Julia's eyes came the glint of a woman's jealousy.

"Darling! Did you leave an address?" she pouted. "I didn't." She set down the coffee which she was about to taste. A roll of bread fell to the floor, toppled off the balcony and fell past storey after storey on to the piazza far below. The bread might have been Julia's happiness falling.

"Darling!" said Henry. "There are things that cannot be neglected and that only I can attend to."

"But I wanted our honeymoon to be *all* honeymoon!" Tears stood in Julia's eyes.

Flitfoot was amazed by the manifestation. Suddenly

Julia's face changed. She wiped her eyes, smiled, laughed her contrition.

"Of course darling," she said, kissing him again. "It was silly of me. I quite understand. I'm a serious woman really. So say you forgive me."

Flitfoot, entirely reassured, squeezed her hand on which gleamed the new wedding-ring.

"But don't open your mail now," Julia begged.

"I won't" said he.

A group of minstrels on the balcony began to sing and play a love-song of Verdi's with all the lyrical ardour of the south.

"Give me some money, darling!" said Julia.

He gave her five francs and a ten-franc note. She screwed the coins into the note, leaned over the balcony, made a sign, and launched the largesse downwards.

"But you *are* opening them!" said she, pouting once more.

"No, darling. I was only cutting the envelopes." Henry instantly ceased to cut. He had the air of a schoolboy detected in naughtiness.

The honeymoon was restored to its pristine perfection.

Then a waiter appeared in the window. The waiter handed a card. It was the card of Mr. John Champ Curtiss, and on it were written the words: "Very urgent. Introducing Mr. Alan Wyatt."

Julia looked over her Harry's shoulder.

"John Champ Curtiss. Who's that?"

"Only a business connection," said Flitfoot casually. "Who Wyatt is I haven't a notion.... Show him up," he added to the waiter.

When Mr. Alan Wyatt arrived on the balcony, he seemed to have come straight from some all-night fancy-dress ball, in which he had disguised himself as an aviator.

He saluted.

"Mr. Flitfoot? I was asked to hand this letter to you personally, sir."

And he handed a letter to Flitfoot.

"Excuse me," said Flitfoot to his wife, before opening the letter. He read: "Dear Harry. It's absolutely imperative that you should come to London at once. The messenger will bring you. Yours J.C. Curtiss."

"Back in a moment," said Flitfoot to his astonished and alarmed wife, and withdrew with the messenger into the drawing-room.

"You've flown over?" he demanded of Alan Wyatt.

"Yes, sir. I ought to have arrived last night, but it got dark. I had to come down at Toulon. I've flown from Toulon this morning."

"Where is your aeroplane?"

"About two miles off. I hired a car to come to the hotel."

"Are you ready to start back immediately?"

"Yes, sir. I've got both food and fuel on board."

"Sit down, will you? Have a cigarette."

Flitfoot rushed into his bedroom, put on a jacket to match the rest of his suit, and rushed back to Julia on the balcony.

He felt that the most difficult task of all his life lay in front of him. He loathed leaving his wife; but those mysterious cords were drawing him again, drawing him away from her. He must go. The strongest part of him desired to go. But he had to persuade Julia to stay.

"Read that, darling," he said, giving the letter to Julia. She read it. The sheet trembled in her hand.

"But–" she quavered.

"Only a great man could have written that letter, darling! Not a word wasted in explanation! The thing must be very serious. And you can see that he counts on me. The aeroplane is waiting."

"Aeroplane!" Julia murmured, feebly aghast.

"I needn't go into details now. I'm frightfully sorry, darling! But it's a very big affair. Millions, perhaps."

"What are millions?" she cried. "We've got all the money we want. We shouldn't be any happier if we had forty millions."

"Darling, I know all that. I am not interested in money. But when I have made up my mind to do a thing, I must have my way and nothing must stop me. And Curtiss is counting on me. I can't let him down." He spoke persuasively, yet with domination.

"But what's the trouble?"

"I don't know," said Flitfoot. "I wish to heaven I did know. I can't think what it is." His face showed anxiety. "All I can say is that neither Curtiss nor anybody else shall stop me from getting where I want to get."

"But our honeymoon! Our *honeymoon*!"

"A honeymoon is one thing, and carrying an enterprise through and doing your duty to a business associate is another."

"But I won't let you go!" cried Julia.

"Darling!" said Flitfoot in a new tone. "Sit down. Now sit *down*."

She obeyed. He drew the other chair close to hers and sat by her side. He seized her hand.

"Look at me! Look into my eyes!" said he gravely. "You told me just now you were a serious woman. You are. I know it. I know you would not have me fail in my duty, at the very beginning of our marriage. What would people think if I said that I must neglect my duty because I was on my honeymoon? What would *you* think of a man that did that?"

Julia made no reply.

Flitfoot continued:

"Darling, do you believe that I love you?"

"Yes." Very feebly.

"Then you know as well as I do that I hate leaving you. Hate it! Hate it! But I should hate more to think that in an unexpected crisis I couldn't rely on my darling wife to help me to do what I *must* do."

"I'll come with you," said Julia, not defeated, but making a strategical retreat.

Flitfoot shook his head.

"No!" said he. "It isn't a woman's job, this isn't. Dangerous!"

"But it's just as dangerous for you," Julia protested.

"Oh, I shall be all right. Listen. I'll fly back here tomorrow or the day after. In two days at most I'll be back again, and you'll think of me all the time and I'll think of you all the time."

The minstrels ceasing to sing and play, left the piazza down below.

"And you shall come with me to the aeroplane. It's all ready, waiting," Flitfoot added.

"But I'm not dressed!"

"What a wife!" Notwithstanding his secret anxiety Flitfoot laughed, and playfully touched her cheek. "She can't see her poor husband off because she isn't properly dressed. Why! You delicious little thing! Put on a fur-cloak, and come as you are. What does it matter. Don't forget you're brazen.... Now run, run! No, the other window; into your bedroom. Quick! I give you ten seconds. I'll get two overcoats for myself."

Those invisible cords were pulling him more strongly than ever.

On the aviation ground the aeroplane waited. Its propeller

began to revolve. Julia wept.

"I shall be all alone," said she. "Not even Toby. You promised me a dog. But you never gave me one."

Flitfoot put his arm round his wife, and whispered in her ear:

"Do you know why? Because I couldn't bring myself to do it. Because I'm too jealous. Didn't I tell you once I was jealous of Toby? I want all of you. I couldn't share you."

She smiled, curiously happy despite her grief.

Flitfoot ascended into the plane, and, his face a strange mixture of gravity and gaiety, waved to his wife, who could not find a handkerchief to wave back. Not an instant had been lost.

The plane started to taxi over the uneven ground. All Flitfoot's hard-set muscles seemed to be pushing it along. It rose. It climbed into the sky. It vanished over the granite summit of a hill. The sound of it died away.

Julia, in her bedroom slippers and stockingless feet, walked to the waiting motor-car which would return her to the hotel. She cried quietly. The episode had been so sudden in its beginning and so sudden in its close that she could hardly credit that the world about her was a real world, and not the creation of an evil dream.

CHAPTER XXIV

Sir Joshua was once more summoned, by telephone and rather peremptorily, to the Managerial room of the head office of the British Standard Bank, where he found himself in the presence of exactly the same group of officials as before. The only difference was that the electric king of London felt himself, appreciably more than the first time, to bear a far closer resemblance to a prisoner in the dock than to a great City magnate.

The General Manager said, after very formal greetings:

"We have come to the conclusion, after careful enquiries, that the shares which you are buying stand already at a price higher than their real value. And as they are still rising we are convinced that you have rivals in the market. We have, therefore, with much reluctance, come to a definite decision that we can grant you no further accommodation on any terms. I thought it only right and fair to make this quite clear to you. No doubt you will be able to make other arrangements."

"No doubt," Sir Joshua agreed, more weakly than he had intended. Somehow he could not control the tone of his voice. "And," the General Manager proceeded, "we shall be greatly obliged if you will take measures to pay off the whole of our loan at the earliest possible moment."

Sir Joshua wanted to argue; but he could find nothing effective to say. At last he said:

"Certainly. Certainly. Of course. Of course."

The General Manager offered no further remark, and his silence was an intimation to Sir Joshua that the interview, so far as the General Manager was concerned, was at an end.

Sir Joshua had no alternative but to rise, shake hands, and depart. Ten minutes had elapsed; but Sir Joshua felt ten years older, for he had not the least idea what he should do to get himself out of the horrible mess without acknowledging that he was a beaten man. And he could not bear to acknowledge his defeat to that redoubtable underling Mr. Forfar, whose advice he had consistently flouted for months past. He took the course which men of infirm purpose usually do take – the course of delay. In any case he could buy no more shares. The vast scheme was at a standstill.

CHAPTER XXV

At about five p.m., on the day of its departure from the Mediterranean coast, after a flight of less than seven hours, the special aeroplane landed at Croydon.[1]

The landing provided a thrill for expert spectators on the ground, for one of the wheels of the under-carriage did not function properly as it touched earth, and a smashing accident might have occurred – but did not. The passenger scrambled out of the machine, with the same celerity with which he had scrambled into it. Asked whether he was hurt, he replied impatiently that he was not hurt, having suffered only a slight jar of his body against the steel frame-work of the cockpit. He walked with some uncertainty, which uncertainty he still more impatiently assured enquirers was due partly to stiffness of limbs after prolonged sitting and partly to the dizzy feeling caused by a whole day of incessant, deafening noise. He gave the aviator a warm, friendly smile of thanks and adieu, walked quickly to the offices, shedding one of his overcoats on the way, passed through the customs like a flash, secured a waiting automobile, threw an order to the chauffeur, and in a little less than no time was hurrying towards London.

"Seems in a bit of a hurry!" said one employé sardonically to another.

He reached Belgravia Mansions, flew up in the lift to his flat, pushed the drawing-room bell with tremendous force, demanded that a meal with champagne should be served instantly, changed into evening dress, ate and drank, flew down in the lift, drove to the Grand Babylon Hotel, asked the number of Mr. John Champ Curtiss's suite, and rang the bell thereat. The door opened, he mentioned his name, and was shown into one of the finest private dining-rooms of the

Grand Babylon Hotel.

At the moment of entering his entire demeanour was suddenly transformed. Outside the drawing-room he had been a man in a fever of terrific haste. Inside he was a slow-motion London idler who had nothing on earth to do and always had had nothing on earth to do and always would have nothing on earth to do.

John Champ Curtiss was just finishing dinner, in the society of a very handsome, elegant, and well-preserved lady, who might have been excused for giving her age as thirty-five. "Well, John!" Flitfoot greeted the American, with an admirably languid and casual air.

"My wife, Mary," said Curtiss.

Pleasant greetings were exchanged. The lady was very gracious.

"You'll be hungry after your journey, Mr. Flitfoot," said she.

"No thanks. I've dined - at my flat."

"When did you leave the Côte d'Azur?"

"Oh! A bit after ten o'clock this morning," answered Flitfoot negligently.

And he accepted a cigar and a glass of port. The lady was perfectly charming to him; she was also perfectly charming to her husband, who was perfectly charming to his wife.

Presently Mrs. Curtiss said, rising:

"I understand that you two have business together, so if you'll excuse me I'll leave you to it."

Flitfoot thought he had never met a more urbane and agreeable creature. Mrs. Curtiss had all the experience and the aplomb which his darling Julia had yet to acquire. He opened a door leading into another room and bowed the enchantress out. Nevertheless somewhere at the back of his mind was an obscure idea that she might be one of those women who take everything for granted - even for instance, the magically swift flight of a man from the Riviera coast to a London hotel.

"I'll say this," remarked Mr. Curtiss. "You didn't let the grass grow under *your* feet."

"What's up, John?" Flitfoot demanded in a new abrupt tone, ignoring the millionaire's compliment. "You wanted me at once. I'm here. But I've got to return."

Mr. Curtiss gazed at Flitfoot, summing up as well as he could this individually enigmatic and powerful man, whose moods seemed capable of changing as bewilderingly as a woman's.

"I'm through with this electric affair, Harry," said Mr. Curtiss at length, imitating Flitfoot's curtness.

"You mean you want to get out?"

"I mean I want to get out."

"But you can't get out."

"But I *shall* get out."

"John," said Flitfoot. "Do you remember what you said when we came to an understanding?"

"Not exactly," Mr. Curtiss admitted, hesitatingly.

"*I* remember exactly. You said I could bet my shirt you'd come out on top."

The arch millionaire recovered his nerve and laughed.

"Then I'll buy you another shirt," said he. "You've lost the one you're wearing."

"I don't understand this," said Flitfoot, simply.

"I'll explain it," said Mr. Curtiss, with equal simplicity.

"The thing's been going splendidly. I know that, though you've never troubled me with any details," said Flitfoot.

"It has," said Mr. Curtiss. "I've put several million dollars into it already. My various agents have been very clever indeed. And the thing *has* been going splendidly."

"Well, then?"

"My wife is against it."

Flitfoot recalled the arch-millionaire's previous references to his wife. He now suddenly comprehended their full significance. Nevertheless he was amazed. Had this urbane and equable enchantress got the great capitalist under her thumb? Evidently she had. Was she twisting the financial Titan round her finger? Evidently she was.

Flitfoot thought:

"If she was my wife, I should give her a lesson once for all."

But he said nothing.

Mr. Curtiss continued, somewhat abashed despite his terrific eminence in the world of dollars:

"It's like this. My wife's father and her two brothers have started a scheme twice as big as yours in New York and Berlin. And I'm asked to come into it. It's the biggest thing the earth has ever seen. I can't carry both schemes, and my wife says that as a patriotic 100 per cent American I ought to choose the American scheme before the British. Is there any answer to that?"

"I don't know."

"Besides, *she* wants it."

"There's an answer to *that*," said Flitfoot boldly.

"You're wrong, Harry. There isn't. You can't judge. You've only been married a week or less. I've been married 20 years, and I reckon to know what I'm talking about."

"I see," said Flitfoot. He did see.

"I asked you to come over quick, because we must leave for Berlin tomorrow, to meet my in-laws. And my notion was that I ought to tell you face to face."

"Your notion was correct, my boy," said Flitfoot. "Then you'll unload all the shares you've got?"

"That's about the size of it."

"At once?"

"As soon as I can. But I don't intend to drown the market, you bet."

"I shan't bet anymore," said Flitfoot drily.

"Once bitten, twice shy, eh?" Mr. Curtiss cynically retorted. He added: "After all, you aren't going to lose anything."

"Yes I am," said Flitfoot. "I'm going to lose my game. And I've never lost a game yet. This is the first shirt I've been robbed of, and I don't like it. Wait a moment, will you?"

Those mysterious cords drew his left hand into his breast-pocket and then drew them out again holding a pocket-book. He opened the pocket-book and took out and unfolded a piece of paper. It was a list of securities in which Julia's fortune was invested. He thought of the urbane and agreeable enchantress in the next room. Was he, Flitfoot, under the thumb of Julia, or was Julia under his? He knew the answer to this question.

"Well, John," said he very quietly. "You'd better unload on to *me*. It's the best you can do."

"Unload everything?" The breath of the arch-millionaire was taken away.

"Not all - at least not all at once," said Flitfoot calmly.

"How much now?" Mr. Curtiss enquired.

"Half a million. Three quarters. Call it four million dollars – as a beginning."

"You mean that?"

"I mean it, my lad. But you'll unload at the price you paid. Not at market prices today."

"Oh of course.... And the rest?"

"Give me an option for six months."

"Six months?.... Er, yes."

"And you'll let me have the use of those clever agents of yours?"

"Why! Sure!"

"What time do you leave for Berlin tomorrow?"

"Two o'clock."

"Well. Perhaps you could look in at my office in the morning and we'll settle a few details - if Mrs. Curtiss can spare you."

Soon afterwards the enchantress brought her delicious scents back into the room.

"You've settled your business?" she asked, with a marvellous imitation of naïve innocence.

"Yes, thanks," Flitfoot answered quickly. "Everything O.K."

But he said to himself:

"She's the most ruthless creature I have ever come across."

"Good night, Mrs. Curtiss," said Flitfoot. "Charmed to have made your acquaintance."

"Must you go?" she twittered.

"I must," said Flitfoot. "I'm tired, though I've only travelled eight hundred miles today."

In the lobby of the suite, showing him out, Mr. Curtiss thus addressed Flitfoot:

"You're a he-man." And he patted Flitfoot's shoulder.

Flitfoot shrugged his shoulder deprecatingly.

"If you mean that I know what I want, I am," said he.

"You're a he-man," Mr. Curtiss repeated.

But outside the door Flitfoot said to himself, addressing Curtiss in Curtiss's absence:

"I can't say the same for you."

CHAPTER XXVI

The next morning Mr. Henry Flitfoot had a tremendous interview in his own office with Mr. John Champ Curtiss, in which all arrangements were made for the transfer of Mr. Curtiss's London electrical interests to himself. His goodbye to Mr. Curtiss was triumphant. At the end of the interview, when Mr. Curtiss had gone, Flitfoot rang for Miss Sligo, and said to her:

"I want to telephone to my wife at the hotel at Cannes. Get me the connection."

"You're in pain," said Miss Sligo. "And you look very tired."

"That's not the point," said Flitfoot.

"No," said Miss Sligo. "But it's one point."

She left him and proceeded to work to obtain the connection. While she was doing it, Flitfoot telephoned to his solicitor:

"I want a power of attorney from my wife to myself to act on her behalf for two years. Her Christian name is Julia. Her address is Belgrave Mansions, London, W.C.1. You understand, full authority to act for her in every way. I want it here in a couple of hours from this moment. Is that clear?"

The solicitor signified that the instructions were clear.

After the usual delays, Miss Sligo obtained the connection to the Riviera.

Flitfoot said to his wife:

"Darling, I love you. I had a splendid journey and I'm very well. I may not be able to get back to you till the day after tomorrow. I shall fly, because I so want to be with you again. My big business is going magnificently, but I may need your help.... No, I haven't seen your father yet. Too busy. I don't think he knows I'm in London."

Julia replied:

"Darling. I shall be so proud to help you. You can't imagine how proud I shall be. But I'm dying to see you and kiss you. I kiss you now, by telephone. Kiss me by telephone too."

And he did kiss his wife by telephone.

"It's a long-distance kiss, my dearest," said he. "But it's a better kiss than ever happened between Curtiss and Mrs. Curtiss."

"You've seen her?" Julia's voice came though the telephone, showing interest.

"I have," said Flitfoot. "She's pretty enough; but I'd as soon kiss a thermometer at zero as her. Well, *au revoir*, darling. You *are* a darling, you know, and *my* darling."

The chat was over in six minutes.

Flitfoot was excited and exceedingly happy.

He rang for Miss Sligo again.

"I'll dictate some letters," said he. "But perhaps I'd better go to Somerset House first about that disputed claim of what's-his-name."

"Mr. Swainson can do that," said Miss Sligo.

Mr. Swainson was Flitfoot's head-clerk. He was so high up in the Flitfoot world that he regarded Miss Sligo as far beneath his notice; but she had her own private opinion of him.

"He can't do it," said Flitfoot.

"He can try. You're in pain," Miss Sligo repeated.

"It's nothing," said Flitfoot. "I got a bit of a jar in the chest yesterday afternoon when we came to earth. Muscle strained. It's nothing."

"You ought to go home and lie down," said Miss Sligo.

"I shall do no such thing," said Flitfoot.

Miss Sligo replied:

"Either you walk out of this office, Mr. Flitfoot, or I do."

The upshot was that Flitfoot, who was in considerable pain, which no happy, victorious excitement could allay, did walk out of his office. At bottom the conqueror was afraid of Miss Sligo when she adopted a certain tone. Also, he was aware that she always meant what she said.

Thus he went home to his flat, as to which no new arrangements had yet been made. It was as untidy as ever. Something told him that he ought to retire to bed. He did retire to his bed.

Miss Sligo's first act, after Flitfoot's departure, was to telephone for a doctor to visit the flat.

As Flitfoot lay in bed giving orders to a waiter, there was a ring at the door, which the waiter had opened. Miss Sligo walked into his bedroom.

"Hello!" said Flitfoot. "Well, I don't think I'll dictate any letters just now."

"I didn't come for that," said Miss Sligo. "I came to see if you were in bed."

"Well, I am."

"You ought to have the doctor."

"Listen to me, Sligo," said Flitfoot. "There's nothing the matter with me except a slight strain. And I absolutely refuse to see any doctor."

"Very well," Miss Sligo agreed, and left the room.

In a few minutes Dr. Brewster, who had once or twice attended Flitfoot, arrived.

Miss Sligo took him into the bedroom.

"Here's the doctor," said she, with the utmost calmness.

Flitfoot submitted. There was no alternative.

CHAPTER XXVII

Dr. Brewster had rather an old-fashioned appearance. He was not young, and he wore a frock-coat instead of the usual morning coat. He spoke slowly and little; and what he did say was said with hesitation.

"There's nothing the matter with me, doctor, except a pain in the chest where I got knocked just a bit against a piece of steel or aluminium or something in the aeroplane."

To this information the doctor made no answer.

He bent over Henry Flitfoot and made a careful examination.

"I don't understand this," he said at length.

"I do. It's perfectly simple," said Flitfoot, quite cheerfully.

"You ought to be x-rayed." [1]

"Oh no!"

"You must be x-rayed."

"Nonsense."

"How long have you been in bed," asked the doctor.

"About half an hour," said Flitfoot.

"You say you feel well?"

"Yes," said Flitfoot.

"Well then, you can get up again and dress," said the doctor.

"You're the sort of doctor I like," said Flitfoot.

"And come with me now to a place in Welbeck Street[2] and be x-rayed.... At once. It won't take long."

"Not on your life."

"It's your life. Not mine."

Flitfoot submitted once more.

He went with Dr. Brewster to Welbeck Street; and in a

large mysterious room at the back of a house apparently on the outside quite ordinary, – a room full of machines and contrivances and another doctor and the latter's assistant and Dr. Brewster, and two nurses, and Miss Sligo (who had silently stuck to him), undressed, lay down, and was x-rayed.

"This afternoon, when the photographs have been developed, I'll call round at your flat," said Dr. Brewster. "Go back to bed now."

For several hours, at his flat, Flitfoot, in bed, dictated letters and memoranda to Miss Sligo, who spent otherwise unemployed intervals in telephoning to the office, and ordering food for Flitfoot and for herself.

At about 5 o'clock Dr. Brewster returned. As he passed into the bedroom he left the x-ray photographs in the sitting-room, with Miss Sligo, and asked her to do some telephoning for him.

"I don't understand it, Mr. Flitfoot," he said to the patient.

"Show me the photographs, and I'll understand it for you," said Flitfoot.

"I haven't them here," said Dr. Brewster.

"Why not?"

"I must have a consultation with a surgeon," said Dr. Brewster, ignoring the question. "And I suggest Sir Andrew Forfar."

"Forfar? Forfar?" The mere name was inimical to Flitfoot. "Who's he?"

"The best man in London for this kind of thing."

"Is he a brother of the fellow in the electricity line?"

"I believe his brother has something to do with electricity supply companies."

"Then I won't have him," said Flitfoot.

"You'd better," said Dr. Brewster. "It's he that I'm suggesting - not his brother. This affair may be serious. I don't say it is, but it may be."

Flitfoot, whose pain had increased, submitted for the third time.

At 7 o'clock Dr. Brewster returned with Sir Andrew Forfar. They expelled Miss Sligo into the corridor and talked in the sitting-room. Then they let her in, and proceeded to the patient's bedroom.

Flitfoot was startled. At the first glance he thought that Sir Joshua Forfar had entered, so remarkable was the resemblance between the two brothers. From that instant he both hated and feared Sir Andrew.

The patient was examined anew. The two doctors, without a word, then returned to the sitting-room, and expelled Miss Sligo anew. Instead, however, of going into the passage, Miss Sligo went into the bedroom.

"What's all this, Sligo?" Flitfoot demanded.

"Who knows?" said Miss Sligo.

"I'm damned if I do!" said Flitfoot.

"You may be damned if you don't." said Miss Sligo.

Her tone made Flitfoot apprehensive.

In the sitting room the two doctors talked together. Dr. Brewster deferential, Sir Andrew Forfar magisterial.

"My theory is," said the great man, photographs in hand, "that the pain is not due to the shock in the aeroplane, if indeed there was any injury. The aeroplane mishap is simply a coincidence. The man's got a swelling as big as a small orange in the blood vessel here. It may be an aneurism of the abdominal aorta. If it is, it might burst and finish him at any moment."

"There's no operation for an aneurism in such a position, I think, Sir Andrew," said Dr. Brewster.

"There hasn't been up to now. But I can perform one and I think it ought to be tried. If it succeeded the news of it would excite every hospital in London." Sir Andrew spoke with an absurd gleeful satisfaction.

"Mr. Flitfoot has a very strong constitution," said Dr. Brewster.

"Evidently. Otherwise I should hesitate, of course," said Sir Andrew. "Has he many friends or relatives at hand?"

"He says not. His wife is on the Riviera."

"No time to get her back. We must act for the best," said Sir Andrew.

In the bedroom, Miss Sligo being present, Sir Andrew said to the patient:

"Dr. Brewster and myself are agreed. It is essential for you to go into a nursing-home immediately –for an operation."

"I won't go," said Flitfoot, sitting up suddenly.

"I advise it," said Sir Andrew.

"So do I," said Dr. Brewster.

"Mr. Flitfoot will go," said Miss Sligo.

"Who'll do the operation?" Flitfoot asked, morally overborne.

"I shall," said Sir Andrew, "of course."

"Are you a surgeon?"

Sir Andrew was obviously hurt by this extraordinary remark.

He, perhaps the most famous surgeon in London, to be asked if he was a surgeon!

"Do you know," said Flitfoot, "that I once nearly killed your brother?"

Sir Andrew gave a sinister smile and replied with dignity:

"As he has dined with us last night I am justified in assuring you that you did not succeed. Moreover, I scarcely see the connection."

"I will cable to Mrs. Flitfoot," said Miss Sligo.

"I forbid it," said Flitfoot.

"Very well," Miss Sligo concurred quietly.

She went into the sitting-room, called the word "telegrams" into the telephone, and cabled to Julia to return at once. She spoke of a slight accident, concluded the message with three words: "Fondest love, Harry."

Then she went back into the bedroom.

"What shall Mr. Flitfoot have to eat?" she asked the doctors.

"Nothing," said Sir Andrew. "What are you thinking of, madam? Food before an operation!"

Within an hour Flitfoot was ensconced in a bedroom in a nursing-home directed by, and owned by Sir Andrew Forfar. He felt that never in all his existence had he been so helpless. The operation was timed for 9 o'clock the next morning.

CHAPTER XXVIII

At 8.45 the next morning, Flitfoot, to the astonishment of everybody, was quite cheerful. He was more than cheerful, – he was chirpy. He said that he had slept nicely, and that though the pain was still present, it was easily bearable. He smiled calmly at the spectacle of Sir Andrew all in white, Mr. Brewster all in white, and two nurses all in white. Sir Andrew held in his sinewy lithe hands a pair of indiarubber gloves.

"I'm ready for anything," said Flitfoot vivaciously.

Although he was hungry he felt very well.

"You have a wonderful nerve," remarked Sir Andrew Forfar, approvingly. Sir Andrew was at least as happy as his patient in the thought of a new and wonderful operation. He had a passion for the knife.

The nurses discreetly smiled their pleasure at the demeanour of this marvellous patient. Dr. Brewster neither smiled nor spoke.

Mr. Henry Flitfoot was lifted on to a mattress which topped a moving framework that ran on indiarubber-tyred wheels. The entire erection was trundled along a corridor to the operating theatre. In the operating theatre he saw yet another man all in white, the anaesthetist; also a scattered collection of basins, sponges, bandages, and some very bright instruments collected on a tray. Further, his nose detected an alarming odour of chloroform or ether or a mixture of the two. Sir Andrew deposited his indiarubber gloves.

Straps were being prepared.

Flitfoot smilingly beckoned Sir Andrew. Sir Andrew approached, and no sooner was he within reach of the patient's arms than Flitfoot sprang up into a sitting posture and with both hands seized the illustrious surgeon by the right wrist and, actuated by those mysterious cords, violently bent the wrist.

Sir Andrew squealed. He ceased to be the illustrious surgeon and became a poor wounded man. Indeed his wrist was bleeding from the indentations of Flitfoot's finger-nails.

"My wrist's broken," shouted Sir Andrew.

Ten hands clutched at the patient, who sank back.

"Sorry!" breathed Flitfoot. "I must have had a nervous fright. I didn't know what I was doing. I hope there's no harm done."

Sir Andrew demanded attention, which he instantly received. An immense confusion! Flitfoot was wheeled back to his bedroom and abandoned. Exulting in his freedom, he put on his trousers and his overcoat and hat.

"Where are you going?" asked a nurse, entering.

"Is that your business?" Flitfoot replied grimly. "I feel rather well, and I take it there won't be any operation today. I'm off home."

"You've broken Sir Andrew's wrist," said the nurse. "His right wrist, too."

"I'm sorry. But you ought to exercise better control over your patients. You wheel them into that slaughter-house and expect them to behave like sheep! The negligence in this place is simply scandalous. I accept no responsibility for it."

He walked downstairs, signalled to a taxi, and drove to Belgrave Mansions.

The next day Miss Sligo, imperturbable, said to him:

"They say Sir Andrew Forfar won't be able to perform an operation for six months - if at all."

"I'm glad to hear it," answered Flitfoot. "I expect he kills on an average about one patient in twenty. I must have saved scores of lives. The fact is, I'm a public benefactor."

The affair was hushed up by the sufferer therein. After all, what could Sir Andrew do? If he brought an action for damages Henry Flitfoot, alive and well and terribly alert, would have made a highly dangerous occupant of the witness-box.

CHAPTER XXIX

On the following afternoon Flitfoot, being in his sitting-room, opened the door to a ring. Julia, in travelling costume, stood at the door – and beside her a porter of the Mansions with a valise.

"Darling!"

"Darling!"

"Then you aren't ill?" Julia exclaimed.

"Never better, darling!" said Flitfoot, taking her by the hand.

At this point the valise was put within the room, and the porter dismissed. Flitfoot also shut the door leading into the bedroom. Then the delightful ceremonials of greetings took place between the happy wife and the happy husband, both of whom, however, were considerably puzzled.

Flitfoot sat in the three-cornered easy-chair, and Julia sat on his knee.

"But dearest," said Flitfoot. "Didn't you get my telegram?"

"Of course! That's why I'm here. I started at once - at least as soon as I could get a berth on the Calais train."

Flitfoot paused, at a loss.

"I suppose you didn't keep my telegram?"

"Didn't keep it? Naturally I kept it, my sweet," said Julia.

"Do you think I would ever destroy any message from you? Here it is."

Julia took the cable from her bag, and Flitfoot read the message which Miss Sligo had despatched to Julia without his knowledge and against his orders, ending with "Fondest love. Harry."

"I see," he remarked, reserving his thoughts. "But I

cabled to you this morning that I should fly over to the Riviera tomorrow."

"Ah!" said Julia. "Of course I didn't get *that* telegram, because I was on my way here."

"I see," remarked Flitfoot once more. "Where's your big luggage?"

"At Victoria."

"Sligo," Flitfoot called aloud; and murmured to his wife:

"Better get off my knee darling. My secretary's in the bedroom packing a bag for me ready for tomorrow morning."

"Packing your bag in your bedroom, dearest!" repeated Julia, astonished.

Miss Sligo entered.

"Oh! Julia," said Flitfoot. "You don't know my secretary, Miss Sligo. Miss Sligo, this is my wife."

He spoke sternly to the secretary. But the curtness of his tone did nothing to soften Julia's intuitive hostility to Miss Sligo, and it did less than nothing to establish a friendly attitude by Miss Sligo towards Julia. Miss Sligo nodded and said naught. Julia said naught and her nod was hardly perceptible.

"Women!" thought Flitfoot. On account of the first telegram, he felt extremely annoyed with the high-handed Miss Sligo; but he managed to conceal his exasperation perfectly.

"Darling!" said he. "Give me the luggage check. Miss Sligo, take this down to Victoria immediately and get Mrs. Flitfoot's luggage out of pawn and bring it here."

Miss Sligo obeyed.

"But dearest," said Julia, resuming her seat on the uncomfortable but beloved knees. "What about this illness? I'm so relieved to find you so well, I can't tell you. But what *was* the trouble?"

"It wasn't," Flitfoot answered.

Then he related his own version of the affair.

"The doctors thought I'd been seriously injured when the plane landed. But I knew I hadn't. And I hadn't. I'm very busy, but I'm in marvellous health. The pain has completely gone."

"And where shall we sleep tonight, my little Julietta?" he asked, a moment later. "We must be practical."

"Sleep? Here of course!"

"But there are only two rooms," said Flitfoot. "This one and the bedroom, plus a bathroom. The bedroom is terribly small."

"It can't be too small, darling," said Julia. "I shall just have to stay here with you – I've often thought of it – until we go down to Oakfield. And while I'm here how easy it will be for me to look after father. Dearest, I should like to be here with you for ever and ever. The place is so tiny and cosy. But I must refurnish it, and make it *really* nice. I shall begin tomorrow morning. Oh darling. I am relieved you aren't ill. And so glad you're so glad to see me." Julia cried a little.

But the next minute she was walking about the flat with him, and explaining what she would do to it. In the bedroom, she seized the packed bag, and unpacked it as violently as though she had been tearing Miss Sligo to pieces.

Miss Sligo returned in about half an hour, her arrival being preceded by bumping noises of heavy luggage in the corridor.

"Shall I *un*pack your bag now?" asked Miss Sligo.

"I have done it, thanks," said Julia, shortly.

"I'll just get my gloves. I forgot them," said Miss Sligo, slipping quickly into the bedroom.

"She doesn't say 'sir' to you, Harry!" observed Julia, smiling.

"Well, she's an old hand, you know," Flitfoot excused his

henchwoman. Then he added: "I say, dearest. I told you, you could be of help to me. I want you to sign a document. Here it is. It must be witnessed, and Sligo could witness it while she's here."

"I'll sign anything," said Julia, ardently truthful.

"But let me explain just what it is," said Flitfoot.

"I *won't* let you, dearest," said Julia, with passionate assertion. "Whatever you want me to do I shall do. Besides, I don't pretend to understand business."

In Miss Sligo's presence Julia signed the power of attorney which gave to her husband full authority to deal as he thought fit with the whole of her property and possessions. Miss Sligo duly returned the deed.

"Shall I order some tea for you, Mrs. Flitfoot?" Miss Sligo enquired.

"No, thank you," said Julia. "I had tea on the train. My husband will order anything I need."

As soon as the secretary was gone Julia began:

"Now I will have a nice blue-grey wallpaper in this room, darling. It will go so well with...." Etc.

She was absorbed in her scheme of decoration and furnishing for the flat.

CHAPTER XXX

One night, some time after Julia had entirely transformed, enriched, brightened and made comfortable the tiny flat, she was sitting side by side with her Harry on a new and very soft sofa in front of the fire, when Mr. Forfar was announced, on a matter of urgency.

Julia shook hands with him very formally, and then said:

"I'll just run up and see how father is." She could with difficulty tolerate the presence of the Scotsman.

"By the way, how's your brother, Sir Andrew, getting on?" Flitfoot enquired as soon as the two men were alone.

"I should advise you not to ask me about my brother," said Forfar darkly, almost savagely.

"Have you and he quarrelled?"

"We have not. But you've ruined his career."

"Well it was a question whether I should ruin his career or he should ruin mine. I won."

"You haven't won yet," said Forfar.

"May I ask why you are giving me the exquisite pleasure of your society tonight, my dear Forfar."

"I'll tell you very quickly. I've found out definitely that somebody is fighting Sir Joshua in the electricity share market."

"Indeed! How clever of you. And who is it?" said Flitfoot.

"You."

"You're quite sure?"

"Quite. Do you deny it?"

"If you're so sure, why do you ask me?" said Flitfoot. "All I say is that it was very thoughtful of you to tell me."

"Various people on your behalf are still buying electric supply shares. And for the purposes of the market you are making use of private and confidential information which you have obtained in your professional capacity as income-tax adviser to our companies." Forfar's manner was decidedly menacing.

"This is really very interesting," said Flitfoot with a smile.

"Yes," continued Forfar. "And you'll be exposed, because I have the proofs of what I say. You'll never survive my exposure. At best you'll be finished professionally. And at the worst you'll find yourself in a court of justice on a charge of criminal conspiracy."

"It's getting quite exciting," said Flitfoot.

"I think I can sustain the conspiracy charge," Forfar went on.

"But why tell me all this?"

"Because I haven't yet told Sir Joshua, and the reason is that I don't wish to make trouble for his daughter."

"Nice of you."

"Hence I'm here to give you the chance to stop your disgraceful operations."

"I'm grateful," Flitfoot murmured amiably.

"What do you say?"

"Me! Now let me see, you observe that door? Well you can open it and depart, my pawky friend."

"You defy me?"

"I don't do anything to you, except request you clear out before I throw you out."

"Very well," said Forfar, rising. "I shall now inform Sir Joshua."

"But just a moment. There's one thing I'd like to mention before you go. Won't you sit down again."

"No, I won't."

"Sit down!" Flitfoot glared at him.

Forfar sat down.

"Talking of private information about your companies obtained by me in my professional capacity as income-tax adviser, I found out one most amusing trifle. I found out that when the West End Electric issued these new shares some while ago, you delayed sending in the notices to shareholders outside England; and also that the wording of the notice was not at all clear. So that many large shareholders either didn't apply at all, or didn't apply in time. Whereas you applied yourself for a large number of shares, and got them allotted in full to yourself; and then when the shares jumped to a big premium you unloaded and got out with a tremendous profit. Which profit amounted to a theft and a swindle, you being the thief and the swindler." He ended: "I have all the proofs. I've been keeping them – for a rainy day. It seems rather a wet night tonight. And now you can go upstairs and inform Sir Joshua. Or you can forget to inform Sir Joshua and run off home. What I do will depend on what you do."

At that moment Julia re-entered the flat.

"Father's asleep," she said to Flitfoot, ignoring Mr. Forfar.

"My dear," said Flitfoot. "You should have come sooner. You'll be sorry to hear that Mr. Forfar has to leave us at once. We had a little matter to discuss, and the discussion didn't take quite so long as Mr. Forfar expected. However, we've come to a clear understanding, haven't we, my dear Forfar?"

"Quite clear," Forfar agreed gloomily.

"Do have a whisky before you go, my dear fellow," Flitfoot urged.

"No thanks."

"But I thought you were a Scotsman."

Mr. Forfar left.

"It's always easier to go downstairs than up," were Flitfoot's final words to him.

CHAPTER XXXI

One night, Flitfoot was walking part of the way home from a dinner of Chartered Accountants which had been held at the Connaught Rooms. He had many free evenings now, because Julia being in a delicate state of health was staying permanently at Oakfield Castle and he saw her only at weekends. He slipped in front of an illuminated shop window on Cheapside, where was a special display of children's footwear. He gazed for some time at a section of the window devoted to shoes for tiny infants, - the tiniest. He seemed to be fascinated by this merchandise.

All the rest of the thoroughfare was dark, save for the street lamps. The traffic was negligible. There was nothing else in the world but himself and these delicate, soft shoes for babies, - and the plate-glass between him and them.

A man, doubtless attracted by the light, stopped by his side in front of the window, coughing. Flitfoot observed out of the corner of his eye that he was a very shabby person, though not very untidy. He turned to walk on towards the West End, and had a full view of the man.

"Chail!" he exclaimed.

Chail recognised him.

Flitfoot shook hands very amiably.

"What are you doing in the City at this time?" he asked.

"I might as well be here as anywhere."

"You look ill," said Flitfoot. "You ought to be in bed."

"I have no bed. And I haven't any money to get a bed, Mr. Flitfoot. I'm at the end."

"You mustn't talk like that, my dear fellow," said Flitfoot cheerfully. "I see you're drinking still. You don't do that without money."

"My last fourpence went that way, sir," Chail frankly acknowledged. And he moved out of the area of the light so that Flitfoot should not see his moral and physical decay.

"Well, I'm very sorry," said Flitfoot. "It's very depressing to see a man with your gifts ruin himself through nothing but lack of character. Why didn't you come and ask me for help?"

He smiled.

Chail answered with the candour of one who has nothing to lose, of one who, as it might be, is already on the scaffold with the noose round his neck.

"Because I knew you were a hard man and you wouldn't help me. I didn't want any more humiliation."

Flitfoot was not in the least offended, or even disturbed.

"My dear Chail," said he. "You were wrong. Of course I will help you. I haven't any money with me, but come along to my office now, and I'll open my safe and see what there is in it."

"God forgive me!" Chail murmured. "I *was* wrong."

He was profoundly touched, in truth he was amazed.

They walked together, and Flitfoot kept the conversation to such exciting general subjects as the weather, one-way streets, and the stock-market. Not a word about himself. Not a word about Chail. Chail began to recover his self-respect under this treatment as an equal.

Flitfoot saw a light in his office, and he was suddenly tempted to use all wariness in entering. The role of spy on his own property appealed strongly to him. He unlocked the main door with careful precautions against the least noise.

"Stay here," he whispered to Chail. "I'll come back to you in a minute. Don't walk about in the corridor."

And he crept towards his private room, and unlatched the door and went in with one stride.

Miss Sligo was seated on his desk smoking a cigar.

Flitfoot maintained his nerve, and Miss Sligo maintained hers.

"Oh! How you startled me!" she greeted him.

"Sorry," he replied evenly. "But you don't show any sign of jumpiness. That smells like a very good cigar. How much do they cost you?"

"Each cigar costs me an evening's work," said Miss Sligo. "I don't know how much my evening's work is worth, because I don't get any extra pay for it."

"And what *is* your evening's work tonight?" asked Flitfoot lightly.

"Much as usual. Forging your signature to your letters. But I've finished. I was just going home."

Both of them knew what the other was thinking. Both of them felt an insincere respect for one another. Both of them were inwardly furious.

"Don't let me disturb you," said Flitfoot. "I ran short of money, and as I'm in for a regular night's orgy, I called in to obtain some cash."

Still smoking her cigar, Miss Sligo moved from the chair, so that her employer could get at the safe.

"Good night," he said, when he had taken ten pounds from the safe and re-locked it.

"Good night," said Miss Sligo. "Pleasant orgy!"

In the corridor near the main door, Flitfoot, talking now in an ordinary tone of kindness, said to Chail:

"See! Here's eight pounds in ten shilling notes and two pounds in silver. I know how awkward it is for fellows in your plight to get change for pound notes and so on."

Chail was astounded. Tears ran down his face as he clutched at the money.

"Sir," he stammered. "I can't say anything. You've saved me."

"I haven't," said Flitfoot cheerfully. "Nothing can save you. Tomorrow you'll be drunk again, and in a day or two you won't have sixpence in your pocket. But I'd like you to be happy as long as you can."

He opened the door. Chail passed out in silence. Flitfoot followed, banging the door.

"Good night," said Flitfoot. "It'll be no use you seeing me again for at least a month. You understand?"

"Yes sir."

The orgy was over.

CHAPTER XXXII

On that same night, very late, Sir Joshua in his dressing-gown paid a call on his son-in-law in the latter's flat. Flitfoot was writing to Julia. The two men, each very busy with his new affairs, had seen very little of one another of late weeks. There had been no Julia to bring them together.

Flitfoot observed with calm, concealed astonishment that Sir Joshua had considerably aged. The electric king of London had no longer a monarchical air. He had the air of a broken man suffering also from solitude and the lack of accustomed sympathy.

"Henry," said Sir Joshua, "I don't feel much like sleep, so I thought I'd come down here for a chat."

Flitfoot gave him some whisky.

"I'm in rather a difficulty –" the old gentleman began.

"Well," said Flitfoot. "If I can be of any help."

"I think you can," said Sir Joshua. "The idea has occurred to me."

The fact was that the idea had been occurring to him with increasing frequency for months.

"My electrical combine isn't going as well as it should. My companies are doing excellent business. Nothing the matter with them. But the combine operation has got to the stage when it needs more capital."

"Well, your Bank will supply that," said Flitfoot.

"That's just what my Bank won't do. My Bank's got two foolish and mistaken ideas into its head. One is that I've been paying too much for the shares I've bought. And the other is that I have a rival in the market – bidding against me. The Bank won't lend me any more. Far from that, it's insisting on repayment of its loans. Indeed the Bank is very pressing indeed. And I've got to see the General Manager next week. He's made an appointment with me."

"How ridiculous it all is!" said Flitfoot sympathetically.

"Glad you think so," said Sir Joshua, eased somewhat.

"But you've got plenty of your own capital left. You must make some sacrifices, daddy."

"I may as well tell you," said Sir Joshua, gazing at the floor, "I haven't got any of my own capital left."

"What! You, a millionaire!"

"Yes. I've used all I had. And I can see the time when I shall be short of ready money." He tried to laugh, adding: "That's only my joke, of course."

"I should say so!" said Flitfoot.

"Now I was wondering whether Julia couldn't let me have – naturally I don't want to worry her just now; but–"

"You needn't worry her. I realised long since that she mustn't be worried by anything. So she gave me a general power of attorney. In all business and legal matters, I'm *her*!"

"So that I can talk to you."

"Most decidedly! Also, I'm her husband."

"Well – er – what do you say?"

"Daddy," said Flitfoot with ingratiating charm, and stopped.

"You said before the wedding that I could always count on her help and yours," urged Sir Joshua.

"Yes," replied Flitfoot. "I know, and we both meant it. But you refused the offer so decisively; you were so sure that everything was all right with you, that –"

"That what?"

"Well, daddy. I'm now using all her money in a very big affair of my own. An affair that I've got tremendous backing for. I won't trouble you with any details. Besides, I promised my partner I wouldn't."

"All Julia's money?" Sir Joshua exclaimed.

"I shall double it. I shall treble it. The thing is going superbly. But I shan't reap the harvest yet."

"*All* Julia's money?" Sir Joshua exclaimed again.

"All."

"Is that quite right?" Sir Joshua became pompous and majestical for an instant.

"It was right when you did exactly the same thing with her mother's fortune. So I suppose it's right for me to do it now."

"But *all*!"

"Well," said Flitfoot. "Haven't *you* used *all* your own resources for a single scheme?"

The old man was silent.

Flitfoot continued:

"I'm frightfully sorry, daddy. If I'd the slightest idea that you'd be in any difficulty I'd have kept every penny of Julia's at your disposal. But I hadn't. You always told me that you had nothing to fear."

"Yes," Sir Joshua mournfully admitted.

"Now look here, daddy," said Flitfoot in a new confidence-inspiring tone. "You're only a bit gloomy tonight. Of course I didn't *advise* you to take up this Combine position. It was only a notion that occurred to me. You remember how careful I was when Forfar tackled me about it that night at dinner upstairs. At the same time, I have the greatest personal belief in your scheme. I feel sure it will be all right. There's no *need* to be gloomy."

"But the Bank?"

"When it comes to the point, the Bank will do as you want it to do. D'you mean to tell me that the British Standard is going to refuse anything to Sir Joshua Massingham? I don't believe it. The Bank is no doubt trying to get money out of you.

Banks always do. They're the greatest bluffers in history. But when you call their bluff – you'll see. Take my word for it."

Sir Joshua responded fairly well to this curative treatment.

Flitfoot finished:

"I'm just writing to Julia. I shan't give her the faintest hint that you've been upset by business matters. And I'm sure you won't either. I shall tell her you came in to see me and were in the pink."

"Quite," said Sir Joshua. "Well, I may be able to sleep now."

"Of course you will," said Flitfoot, and closed the door after him.

CHAPTER XXXIII

A few days passed, and one morning, early, Miss Sligo came into Flitfoot's private office immediately after his arrival.

"I don't need you for the present, Sligo," said Flitfoot.

"I only thought you would be interested to hear a piece of news that I learnt last night," said Miss Sligo.

"At the Bagdad Café, I suppose?" said Flitfoot.

"Yes."

"No, I'm not," Flitfoot replied, in a very casual and matter-of-fact tone.

"Oh!" murmured Miss Sligo.

"Not in the least interested," Flitfoot went on. "I expect I could tell you more than you could tell me, or ever would be able to tell me."

He bent over his desk in a manner to indicate plainly that Miss Sligo's presence in his room might well be spared.

"Sorry I spoke," Miss Sligo muttered, rather defiantly.

She turned to a cabinet of card-indexes and began fussily to rearrange them.

Flitfoot glanced at her once or twice.

"Am I disturbing you?" she asked.

Flitfoot put his hand on the telephone.

"I want to telephone," said he.

"I'm in the way?" she asked, as if affronted.

"You are," he replied.

"Sorry," said Miss Sligo, and walked out of the room in a pet which she took little or no trouble to conceal.

It was clear that the relations between the pair now lacked that mutual understanding and complete confidence which hitherto had been their chief characteristic.

Flitfoot gave a number.

"That you, Samson?"

A voice answered with a laconic affirmative.

Flitfoot said:

"Flitfoot speaking. Sell. Sell a thousand or so. This morning. At any price. Make it plain that you *must* sell."

"Right!" said the voice.

Flitfoot hung up the receiver, took it down again, and gave another number."

"That you, Searle?"

"Yes."

"Flitfoot speaking. Sell 1,500. This morning. At any price. Don't haggle. See?"

"Yes, I see."

Flitfoot hung up the receiver, took it down a third time and gave still another number.

"That you, Massucci?"

"Yes. Who's speaking?"

"Flitfoot. There'll be two or three thousand shares on the floor this morning. Forced sale. Buy 'em. But beat them down. They'll stand it. Tell everybody the price you've paid. Spread it around. See?"

"Yes."

"That's all. Don't ring me up to tell me the price. I'll wait to see it in the paper tonight."

"Yes."

"By the way, heard from Mr. Curtiss lately?"

"Yes. He's still very busy in Berlin."

CHAPTER XXXIV

The same evening Miss Sligo went down into the Bagdad Café and occupied her favourite corner. There was not a soul in the place except the waitress.

"Your friend isn't here yet, miss," said the waitress, after taking Miss Sligo's order for two hot scones, two pats of butter, and China tea with cream.

"What friend?" enquired Miss Sligo very coldly.

"I beg your pardon, miss, I'm sure."

Miss Sligo opened a weekly periodical entitled "The Girl of Today", and began to study it with diligence.

Then Mr. Meacham entered and, removing his silk hat, dropped into his favourite seat at the small table next to Miss Sligo's small table.

"Who'd have dreamt of meeting you?" Miss Sligo addressed him pertly.

Mr. Meacham was somewhat astonished and encouraged by this marked change from her usually self-protective demeanour.

He said, quite gaily – for him:

"I expect you thought I wasn't coming tonight." Then he added quickly, frightened at his own boldness: "I beg your pardon."

"Not at all," Miss Sligo gracefully excused him. "As a fact I was beginning to be afraid you weren't coming. I'm glad you have come, because I've got some news for you."

At that moment the waitress appeared with a tray full of the delicacies of Miss Sligo's desire; and the subject of conversation had to be changed.

"My word!" said Mr. Meacham, gazing at the tray. Then to the waitress: "Same for me, please."

The waitress departed.

"You *are* doing yourself well tonight," said Mr. Meacham.

"Well," said Miss Sligo, "I'll just tell you this – I felt like it. Yes, I felt like it."

"I hope you didn't mind me ordering the same as you," said Mr. Meacham.

"Not in the least," said Miss Sligo. "They do say, imitation is the sincerest form of flattery."

"Well Miss Smythe," Mr. Meacham gallantly replied: "All I know is, I always enjoy it more when I'm eating and drinking the same as you, Don't know how it is, but it's a fact."

"Oh, Mr. Meacham. You do go on at a rate."

A pause.

"You've stopped," said Miss Sligo.

"I didn't want to interrupt your news," Mr. Meacham explained.

"You're dying to hear it?"

"I certainly am," said Mr. Meacham. "Anything that is interesting to you is interesting to me."

"Well," said Miss Sligo. "It's about myself."

"Better and better!" observed Mr. Meacham.

Then the waitress arrived with Mr. Meacham's tray of delight. The girl dawdled about in their neighbourhood so long that before she was out of earshot Miss Sligo and Mr. Meacham, in order to pass the time, were both filling their mouths with hot scones well buttered.

At length the waitress vanished, and the discretely-lit mysterious underground room held nobody save the two in the corner.

"Perhaps you won't be so interested after all," Miss Sligo resumed coyly. "I see no reason why you should."

"Please!"

"It's only that I'm giving up my job," said Miss Sligo.

"Giving up your - !"

Mr. Meacham raised his hands in amazement.

"Yes. The fact is, they don't appreciate me at my place. And as I've saved a bit of money I'm going to take a rest for a while."

"Well I never!" exclaimed Mr. Meacham.

"Yes," said Miss Sligo. "That's the size of it."

"What a shame!" protested Mr. Meacham.

"Shame?"

"I mean what a shame it is they don't appreciate a really fine girl like you."

" 'Girl', you say, Mr. Meacham?"

Something in Miss Sligo's tone inspired him.

"Yes, I do," he insisted.

"Perhaps you're right," Miss Sligo agreed astoundingly.

"Of course I'm right!" Mr. Meacham was a man transformed.

"Yes," said Miss Sligo. "And I shall go back to my right name now."

"Isn't your name Smythe?"

"No. Smythe is only my stage-name," Miss Sligo explained.

"Are you on the stage?"

"I mean it's my *nom de plume*," Miss Sligo explained.

"Are you an author then?"

"I mean it's my professional name," Miss Sligo explained.

"Ah! Yes!"

"You see, Mr. Meacham," said Miss Sligo, "a girl has to protect herself, especially in my job. You've no idea – if your real name gets about then they find out where you live, and I don't know what all! So I called myself Smythe. But my real name is Sligo – Ruth."

"Ruth Sligo - it's a charming name. Almost Irish."

"I have Irish blood in my veins, I believe," Miss Sligo admitted with pride. "I wish I'd told you about my name before," she added. "A girl doesn't like to deceive her friends. But you know how it is. You begin - and you go on, and there you are."

"And so you're going to live all alone?"

"Yes. I suppose so."

"At Ealing?"

"Yes."

"What a pity!" murmured Mr. Meacham.

"Why?"

"There are healthier places. Canterbury, for instance. And there's a house there with more beds than one in it." Miss Sligo made a gesture as if to stay the man's mad course: but Mr. Meacham was not to be stayed.

"I've been admiring you for a long time now. And if you're giving up your job I beg to inform you that I'm not giving up mine. And it's a good one too. And safe. Old Sir Josh may go smash, but my company isn't going smash, nor Mr. Forfar neither. He's on velvet, and so'm I."

At this exciting juncture, not less than four customers entered to disturb the solitude of the Bagdad, and scattered themselves around the big room. So that Miss Sligo and Mr. Meacham had prudently to subdue their chatting to mere murmurs. Hence also they had to edge nearer to one another.

Three of the customers, having hastily refreshed themselves, departed in haste. The fourth sat a long way off.

"Let me pay for both, Miss Ruth," Mr. Meacham daringly suggested.

Miss Sligo shook her girlish head:

"That wouldn't do." After an interval she added, with a strange smile: "If you like I'll toss you for who pays for both."

"There's nobody like you!" said Mr. Meacham, enchanted. "Heads I win, tails you lose."

He drew a coin from his pocket, and very delicately and discreetly tossed.

"Heads!" said he.

It was heads.

"I've lost. I pay," said Miss Sligo.

"Excuse me," Mr. Meacham corrected her. "I won. Therefore I have the pleasure of paying."

"You're very clever, aren't you?" said Miss Sligo, laughing.

"I think I am," Mr. Meacham concurred.

And he did pay.

They went upstairs into the street. And in a dark alley adjacent to Amen Corner, Mr. Meacham, having raised his silk hat, might have been seen (had he and Miss Sligo not taken every precaution not to be seen) placing a discreet kiss on Ruth's girlish mouth.

CHAPTER XXXV

Twenty-four hours before his appointment with the General Manager of the British Standard Bank at the head-office Sir Joshua received a telephone message from the manager of the City branch office of the Bank requesting his immediate attendance at that office, if not inconvenient. As his monarchical motor-car happened to be waiting, he took it and drove away. To all appearances he was still the luxurious millionaire electric King of London; but in the secrecy of his head he guessed that he was driving to his doom.

In the street he happened to catch a glimpse of a newspaper contents bill:

Electricity Shares.
Violent fluctuations.

Although he knew far more than the paper knew, he was none the less affrighted by that contents bill.

The interview with the branch-manager was one of the briefest business interviews that Sir Joshua had ever had.

The branch-manager said:

"Sir Joshua. I'm sorry to say that I've had definite instructions from our head-office. We have long since given you notice to repay. You have asked for time, and you have had time. You cannot say that we have not shown every forbearance. My instructions are that the total of the loans must be repaid at once."

"What do you mean – 'at once'?" Sir Joshua faltered.

"Tomorrow. You've had warning, Sir Joshua."

"But it can't be done."

"Then we shall be compelled to sell the shares which we hold as security."

"Throw them on the market?"

"We shall use every care, naturally, both for your sake and our own. But the shares will be sold - and the sooner the better. Prices are falling."

"They rose yesterday."

"But they've fallen more today. And we anticipate there will be a severe break. We haven't a day to lose."

"I'll go and see the General-Manager," said Sir Joshua.

"Believe me, Sir Joshua. It will be useless. My instructions are final."

"Very well," said Sir Joshua.

He had not been able to think of all the brilliant and effective things that Flitfoot had suggested to him to say. As for calling the Bank's bluff –

Ten minutes later a decrepit, old, haggard man entered the spruce offices of Mr. Henry Flitfoot. It was Sir Joshua Marsington. Flitfoot received him instantly.

"It's all over," Sir Joshua gasped. "The Bank will sell everything tomorrow."

Flitfoot heard the story with sympathy.

"Well," said he. "We must take the rough with the smooth and make the best of it. If all Julia's money wasn't tied up, I'd at any rate keep the bottom from falling out of the market. But, as things are, I can't. However, let's hope for the best."

"I suppose I ought to resign my directorships?" Sir Joshua muttered.

"Safest," Flitfoot agreed. "Especially if the shares don't realise enough to cover the Bank's loans. Of course then they'd make you bankrupt. Yes, you'd better resign."

"And yet all my companies are flourishing."

"Yes, daddy. Everyone knows that. It's *you* that aren't flourishing," said Flitfoot. "Of course a gamble's a gamble. Some win. Some lose. I must see that Julia doesn't hear a word of this. And I say, if you're short of ready cash, just let me know. I can always lay my hands on a few thousands for immediate needs. I shall see you have all you want for your own private purposes. It might be a good thing for you to go and live for a bit in a first rate hotel in Paris or Brussels."

Sir Joshua listened, scarcely hearing.

As soon as he had gone, Flitfoot gave telephonic instructions to Mr. Curtiss's agents, Mr. Samson, Mr. Searle, Mr. Massucci and others, to wait for the break in Electricity shares and then to buy cautiously all the shares they could – of every company – at the lowest possible price.

"Don't hurry," he said. "Nobody's going to be in a hurry to buy London Electricity shares just now. You hang off, and you'll get 'em at your own price."

CHAPTER XXXVI

The next morning, in his private office, Flitfoot was telephoning further instructions to his secret agents when Miss Sligo came in.

"Can't you see I'm telephoning?" said Flitfoot, putting his hand over the mouth-piece of the instrument.

"I thought I was your confidential secretary," Miss Sligo replied tartly.

"What do you mean?"

"You don't trust me any more," said Miss Sligo.

Flitfoot said into the telephone:

"I'm called away. I'll ring you again in five minutes."

Then he fronted Miss Sligo, who in turn fronted him.

"Now listen, Sligo. You and I have come to an understanding."

"Yes we have," said Miss Sligo. "I didn't mind what you did, so long as you trusted me. You might ruin half the City, including your own father-in-law, for all I cared, so long as you trusted me. That was all I wanted – to be trusted."

Flitfoot said:

"I asked you to listen, not to talk, Miss Sligo. I've had rather more than I propose to stand. You smoke my cigars, in my presence. You put rude messages into my cigar-cabinet. You cable all sorts of affectionate messages to my wife in my name, when I've told you positively not to cable anything. You come in here disturbing me when you know you are not wanted. I've been wondering whether it's me or you who's the boss of this office. You ardently imagine you're indispensable. You're mistaken. You'll be good enough to take a month's notice."

"I shan't take a month's notice," answered Miss Sligo fiercely. "Because I don't want a month's notice. I'm going to walk straight out of this office now, this minute. And I'll never come into it again. I wouldn't stay in any place where I wasn't trusted. And if you think I'm dependent on you, you're mistaken. I can get better jobs than this, and if you'd like to know, I've got one already. I knew you meant to give me notice. You don't catch Ruth Sligo napping. Good morning – to you and your cigars."

She vanished. Then she came back.

"But I forgive you," she said, in the doorway. "And I'll send you a slice of my wedding-cake."

This severance was one of the worst blows that Flitfoot ever received. Miss Sligo, in long years, had become a habit of his. And it is very difficult to break an old habit – even a good one.

As Miss Sligo strolled in glorious idleness about the City before getting her lunch, and journeying to her one-roomed abode at Ealing, she saw newspaper contents lists.

One said:

City Sensation
Sir Joshua Marsington
resigns.

Another said:

The
Electric King
abdicates.

CHAPTER XXXVII

In the principal bedroom of Oakfield Castle, a magnificent panelled chamber, Julia and a uniformed nurse were standing by a Queen Anne baby's cot, which, on castors, had been placed near the great Queen Anne bed. All the furniture in the room was of the Queen Anne period.[1] The general aspect of the room might affright the moths at night, but afternoon sunshine through two high windows now filled it with bright yellow sunshine.

The door opened and Henry Flitfoot came in with masculine noise and directness.

Julia turned and saw him.

"Hsh, dearest!" she murmured. "She's not very well. I've had the doctor. It can't be serious, but see how flushed her two dear little cheeks are!"

The nurse moved away; then discreetly quitted the room, leaving the parents alone with the six-weeks-old child.

"I don't think *I*'m very well either," said Flitfoot, as he ardently returned his wife's ardent kiss.

"You! What's the matter?"

"Oh! I suppose it's nothing. Except jealousy. You know how men hate their women to be unwell." He smiled enigmatically.

"You are a tease!" Julia whispered.

"I am," Flitfoot agreed. "And you're more beautiful than ever – far more. It suits you to be a mother, and you've recovered wonderfully."

"Do you *love* me more than ever?" Julia asked.

"Seventy and seven times more," he replied, and as he clasped the woman who less than a year earlier had been a mere girl he felt profoundly that he did love her more than ever.

"There's nothing much wrong with this pleasing infant of yours," he said, as they bent over the cot opposite one another.

"You mothers are all the same. What did the doctor say?"

"He said he didn't think it was anything important," Julia answered.

"Wise fellow!" murmured Flitfoot.

The father was intensely happy. In the Riviera hotel he had imagined that he could never be more happy than he was then. He admitted now that he had been wrong. His happiness, his satisfaction in his wife and tiny child were steadily growing.

"Came down in ninety minutes," he remarked. "Good going."

"Yes, and one day you'll have an accident," Julia commented.

"Accidents don't happen to me," said he.

The nurse returned.

"The lunch-gong has just gone," said the nurse.

"And I'm hungry," said Flitfoot.

He took his adored wife by the arm and led her out of the room.

When lunch was finished and the servants had gone, Julia opened her bag and pulled out a letter.

"Here's a silly, wicked thing I've received," she said, smiling nervously.

Flitfoot read:

"Madam, I know you don't like me, and you will say that this is a letter from a dismissed employee. At any rate it is not anonymous. I think you ought to know that the man who has ruined your father is Mr. Henry Flitfoot. Yours truly, Ruth Meacham (née Sligo)."

Flitfoot folded up this letter and gave it back to Julia.

"I'll tell you everything, darling," said he with an

enchanting smile.

"Then it's true!" she exclaimed, withdrawing the hand which he had taken.

Flitfoot lit a cigarette calmly.

"Of course it isn't true," he said.

"Oh, Harry. Do forgive me. I knew it wasn't."

"In the first place the old gentleman isn't ruined at all. You know and anybody knows that he's retired from his directorships and all business. And he's staying for the present in Paris in considerable luxury. He's a bit gloomy, naturally. But that's because he started out to form his great London electrical combine, and it didn't come off. But ruined he is not."

"Well?"

"But I may as well tell you that if your father isn't the great electric boss that he wanted to be, *I am*, or rather I shall be in a few days, unless something goes wrong. Your father wouldn't believe that anybody was up against him. But somebody was up against him. And a very big somebody: John Champ Curtiss."

"The man you told me of once?"

"Yes."

"Your friend?" Julia looked suspicious.

"My acquaintance. Well, when I knew how things were going, I made use of my acquaintance to save your father. If I hadn't interfered the old man *would* have been ruined. He'd have been bankrupted, without a cent to his name. Well, I got Curtiss to let me take everything over from him. It was a terrific affair to handle, and I couldn't possibly have handled it if I hadn't played for a time the same game that Curtiss himself played. There *had* to be a break in the market, because if the shares hadn't dropped tremendously I couldn't have found enough money to buy sufficient of them. That's clever, isn't it?"

"I think so," said Julia.

Flitfoot proceeded:

"So that your father had to be shaken out, as they call it. Bad for him, of course. But better than ruin and bankruptcy. To help me Curtiss very decently gave me time to square up with him – Curtiss. I control now all the shares your father bought and a fine lot more besides. And that's thanks partly to the use of your money and partly to Curtiss's good nature."

"But why couldn't you have let father do it for himself?" asked Julia.

"Now darling. I know you adore the old man, and I'm rather fond of him. But I must be frank with you. He couldn't have done it for himself. He hadn't the sort of brain to do it for himself. When he began to make a noise in the world he had one or two good flukes in using your mother's money. He made a name and he kept the name by looking wise and saying as little as he could."

Julia's face momentarily changed.

"Now don't be cross with me, my pet," Flitfoot soothed her. "It's true. He was able to retain all your mother's money intact by luck. That money came to you. I've used it again. And I shall return it to you not only intact but doubled, more than doubled. I've saved your father from a complete smash into the bargain. If your father had had the use of your money, he'd have lost it all, just as he's lost all his now. He could never have beaten Curtiss. The poor old man is past work – everybody in the City knows that." Flitfoot added lightly: "We'll allow him ten thousand a year or so, and he won't have anything to complain about. But for heaven's sake don't tell him what I've told you!"

"Darling!" Julia murmured. "You frighten me. But I'm sure you acted for the best. I must go back to baby."

She rose.

"Girl!" Flitfoot stopped her. "Angel-girl! One moment. I've nearly succeeded. I intend to control all the electric lighting and power in London. I've got a majority of shares in seven companies out of fifteen, or I soon shall have. I shall be the electric king that your father never was and never could be. *But*, I'm not yet quite, quite out of the wood. I've still a trifling settlement to arrange with the Titan Curtiss. I thought I could do it better here, with you near me, than in London. I can always do better if you are near me. And that's why I've asked him and his wife to drive down by ten. They'll be here early. But I wrote to you about that."

CHAPTER XXXVIII

After a grand afternoon tea in the English manner which Americans so much admire, Flitfoot and Julia, urged to do so by Mr. and Mrs. Curtiss, displayed the wonders of Oakfield Castle.

Mrs. Curtiss, as she walked from room to splendid antique room, became more and more gracious and more enthusiastic. She had never seen a house so complete, so perfect, and her laudatory adjectives multiplied like rabbits. Julia admired her dignified and calm style immensely, envied it, and was rather intimidated by it.

The party reached the principal bedroom, and duly admired the baby. Mrs. Curtiss admired the baby with rapture, having no offspring of her own. She confessed that she envied Julia with a marked envy. And Julia was flattered to be the object of her envy. Nevertheless into her innocent heart crept the suspicion that Mrs. Curtiss admired the bedroom more than the baby. Julia tried to chase this suspicion out of her heart; but she did not succeed.

Having inspected the interior of the Castle, the splendid Mrs. Curtiss had to inspect the exterior. She walked with her husband round and round the façades. And then she walked round and round the ancient gardens.

At length, as dusk began to fall, John Champ Curtiss made a sign to Flitfoot that they two would do well to hold their business conference. After the American had had a word with his wife, Flitfoot led first into the house, up to the second storey, to a small, dingy and untidy little room.

"My den," said Flitfoot.

"Different from the rest of the house," Curtiss commented.

"Yes," said Flitfoot. "But you see I don't care where I live. If I *have* a preference, it's for this kind of a place. I don't give a hang for luxury. I leave that to women. See?"

"Yep," said Curtiss.

They sat down to a conversation about business, serious business, the most serious business.

"You've done very well, Henry," said Curtiss after Flitfoot had talked for a while. "I couldn't have done the job better myself. And you're thorough."

"I'm not quite thorough," said Flitfoot. "Because I still owe you £150,000, and it's due on Monday."

"Oh! That's a trifle for you, now."

"It will be a trifle for me in a month's time. But it isn't a trifle just at the moment. I'm hanging on by the skin of my teeth. I've borrowed every cent I can. On adequate security, of course. Still, I can't borrow any more."

"I have just got to have three quarters of a million dollars from you on Monday, Henry my boy," said Curtiss, very firmly. "I'm counting on them. If you're hanging on by the skin of your teeth, perhaps I am too. The Berlin-Paris-New York merger is the biggest thing I was ever in, by a long sight."

"Well," said Flitfoot, with his ingratiating smile. "I've got a sort of suspicion you won't have three-quarters of a million dollars from me on Monday. You can have them in a month."

"Monday is the date."

"I'm not denying it. But can't is can't."

"Do you want to drive me to being drastic?" Curtiss demanded.

Greek was meeting Greek.

"Now look here, John. Don't be unreasonable. What's a month to you?"

"It's everything to me. You must borrow more from somewhere. Borrow on this castle of yours, for instance."

"Can't. I've mortgaged it already for all I could," said Flitfoot. "I might pawn my shirt, if that would help."

"What's it worth?"

"Thirty shillings," said Flitfoot.

"I meant the castle, furniture and everything."

"Money couldn't buy a place like this," said Flitfoot cautiously, remembering with a secret smile that he had bought it from his father-in-law for £30,000.

"I'll give you the £150,000 for it," said Curtiss suddenly. "Then we shall be square and all smooth. My wife has gone mad about it. And I'd love to make her a surprise present of the entire homestead as it stands. She likes a surprise present now and then. Now. That's an offer."

"But you've just told me you're hanging by the skin of your teeth and that three quarters of a million dollars is the difference between life and death to you, and so on and so on."

"Never mind that," said Curtiss in the warning tone of an arch-millionaire who objects to being cross-examined. "I make you the offer. Haven't *you* just told me that you don't care where you live, and you hate luxury, and prefer squalor, and so on and so on."

Flitfoot laughed.

He was about to say: "My wife is very fond of this house. I daren't sell it." But he did not say it, for the reason that he remembered Curtiss's extraordinary subservience to Mrs. Curtiss. He emphatically did not want to put himself, as a husband, on the despicable level of John Champ Curtiss.

Curtiss divined that he had won. As for Flitfoot, Flitfoot's soul was uplifted by the sublime assurance that his kingship of the electricity of London was now an accomplished fact.

Then, as he had said nothing to indicate that he accepted Curtiss's offer, he wavered for a few moments in his mind. But the invisible, mysterious cords drew him irresistibly to the little desk, where he wrote out in duplicate a contract note by virtue of which Curtiss agreed to cancel the outstanding liability of £150,000 and Flitfoot agreed to hand over Oakfield Castle and all its appurtenances within a fortnight.

They both signed, and each man pocketed the duplicate signed by the other.

"That's what I call doing business quick," said Curtiss; and he added, with finger lifted: "Not a word to Mrs. Curtiss. I mean to give her the thrill of her life."

He drove back to London with his tyrant, smiling to himself.

That night the young mother slept alone with her baby in the cot by her side. She had fed the infant, and the infant was assuredly better.

Flitfoot entered the chamber to bid his wife a good night. He sat intimately on the bed, and chatted, and Julia was very happy.

"You like to have me here, old girl," said Flitfoot bending over her.

"Oh, Harry!" Julia lovingly protested at such an absurd question.

"With you and Baby," she murmured, "I wouldn't mind where I was. I'd live in a semi-detached villa in Golder's Green[1] and be happy."

Flitfoot laughed and changed the subject.

Later he said:

"You know, child. I've had a dashed near shave with Curtiss. He's as hard as marble."

"But you beat him," said Julia admiringly. "I can see it in your face."

"Yes. But to stop him from doing something drastic, I had to do something drastic myself."

He then told her what he had done and that by doing it he

had at least doubled her fortune, and incidentally made himself the king of all London's electricity.

Julia burst into tears.

"We'll go and live for a bit in your father's flat. There's plenty of room there, and he'll never use it again," he reassured her. "Then I shall see you every night and every morning."

Julia still wept.

"You said you simply didn't care where you lived so long as you're with me," he argued.

"I don't – of course I do – really," she said. "But I'd give in to you, if it wasn't for Baby."

"Baby! Baby's all right."

"You say we shall have to leave here in a fortnight at the latest?"

"Yes. And why not?"

"Baby isn't all right. She's all ups and downs. She won't be all right for weeks and weeks. And if you think I'm going to risk taking her to London in less than a fortnight, you never were more mistaken in your life!"

Julia sat up in bed: the tigress at bay.

Flitfoot was genuinely startled.

The raised voice of her mother had disturbed the infant, who moved in the cot. Julia, forgetful of everything else, soothed her with outstretched arm.

"You must go, Henry," said Julia. "Please! At once!"

And Flitfoot left the room.

The next morning, dressed and talking to the nurse, Julia looked like a woman who had not slept all night.

Flitfoot came in.

"Baby is much better," said the nurse to baby's father. "Very much. She's had a grand night, but Mrs. Flitfoot hasn't, I'm sorry to say." She wheeled the cot out of the room into the bathroom.

Flitfoot fondled his wife very tenderly. "I'm fearfully ashamed of myself, darling," he said, as she began to relent. "The mischief is that I've signed a definite contract with Curtiss, to give him possession of the whole bally place. And he can enforce it. And he will too. There'll be the most horrid trouble. And now Baby's so much better. In fact quite well -"

His gaze dominated her.

He stayed three full days with Julia at Oakfield. He began to make arrangements for the great exodus from the Castle. Baby continued to improve. Julia's resistance was worn down. Before the expiration of the fortnight, the exodus was accomplished. The Flitfoot family installed itself in Sir Joshua's flat; and Flitfoot was highly and openly content.

But Julia said to him once, *à propos* of nothing:

"You're fonder of being the electric king than you are of Baby and me. I'm so afraid of you, Henry."

He gazed at her.

Then she cried, and clung to him.

"You're absurd, my sweetest pet," said he with a sudden smile. "You're mixing up two things that oughtn't to be mixed up. Love is one thing, and doing what you've made up your mind to do is another. I told you on our honeymoon –"

"Stop!" Julia exclaimed. "I've heard it all. Don't tell me again."

She wept anew, and tightened her convulsive grip on him.

CHAPTER XXXIX

One afternoon Mr. Flitfoot went into the offices of the West End Electricity Supply Company, and demanded immediately the presence of Forfar, which presence he immediately obtained in the important room formerly occupied by Sir Joshua Massington.

"You've installed yourself here?" said Flitfoot sharply to Forfar.

"Well, Mr. Flitfoot, I'm in charge, since Sir Joshua left."

"You won't be any longer," said Flitfoot. "You'd better go back to your own room. I shall be in charge in future. Let me try that chair."

"But –" Forfar began.

"There is no 'but'," Flitfoot cut him short. "If you don't know already, you very soon will know, that I now control a majority of shares of this Company. I shall therefore have myself elected to the Board and then to the chairmanship of the Board. The same thing will happen to six other companies. A mere matter of form."

"I see," said Forfar, vacating the chair at the desk which had once been Sir Joshua's.

"You see! Your eyesight is good," replied Flitfoot. "I will tell you something else. The seven companies will be consolidated, and in due course the remaining London electricity supply companies will come in, because they'll have to. And I, and nobody else, shall be the big noise in all London's electricity. I won't say any more, – I don't care much for boasting."

Flitfoot tried the chair.

"Yes," said he. "This chair is very good. Like a throne!"

He glanced round the plain, large room, on whose walls

were hung photographs of the exteriors and interiors of various generating stations.

Forfar stood in attendance.

Flitfoot opened one or two drawers in the desk.

"Have these drawers emptied," he ordered.

"Certainly, sir." Forfar's manner had changed.

"And I say, Forfar," Flitfoot called as Forfar was leaving.

"Yes, sir."

"There's a man named Meacham here."

"Yes, sir. Sir Joshua's secretary. A very satisfactory man. Not afraid of work. Been with us a very long time."

"Too long," said Flitfoot. "He must go. Sack him."

"May I ask why, sir?"

"Because I want him to be sacked. He's got married. He talks too much to his wife, and she talks too much. He's the slave of the woman. Not his fault. I'm sorry for him. Tell him he shall have a pension – two thirds of his salary. He shan't be able to say that he hasn't been treated generously."

"Yes, sir."

"I'm going out now. I'm beginning at once to make a round of all my generating stations, and I shall start with the West End. Don't know when I shall be back. Wait for me."

Flitfoot went out to his car.

Forfar respectfully accompanied him.

"Aren't you working too hard, sir?" said Forfar on the pavement ingratiatingly.

"Yes," said Flitfoot. "But it won't be for long. When I've got things in order–"

"You look a bit tired, sir."

"I am tired," Flitfoot coldly admitted. "But I shall be all right again in a month at the latest."

"Running all these companies and your own business as well–" Forfar continued.

"Don't let that trouble you. I'm selling my own business," said Flitfoot. "Managing London's electricity will be a whole time job, even for me."

He laughed. Forfar made haste to laugh also.

Flitfoot drove off. Those invisible cords seemed to be pulling forward the chauffeur himself, and the car too. But Flitfoot did feel tired, and the sensation of fatigue rendered him uneasy. He consoled himself with the cherished thought of Julia, whom he had left in the early morning. She had been talking the usual talk - the dear worrying creature - about Baby being not quite well. But he knew that Baby had a fine constitution and was at least as healthy as any infant only a few months old has the right to be.

It appeared to him that the car took hours and hours to reach the generating station. However, it did in the end arrive there.

Ignoring the door-keeper, Flitfoot strode masterfully into the vast, dim, roaring, rumbling interior. The cords positively dragged him inside. Another, but a weaker, force within him was ineffectually trying to prevent his entrance.

"Send the manager to me," he said to the door-keeper. "My name is Flitfoot and don't forget it. I'm the new chairman of the Company."

"I can't leave my post, sir," the door-keeper protested.

"Did you hear me?" said Flitfoot.

The door-keeper left his post.

Flitfoot walked to and fro past the colossal series of dynamos. He gloated over the immense machinery, some of it moving so rapidly that its motion could scarcely be detected, other parts of it moving with the deliberation of a leviathan.

He was a pigmy in the lofty, wide-spreading, resounding, pulsing interior. And yet in fancy he felt himself a giant, towering to the roof, dominating the monsters of steel.

The manager arrived.

Flitfoot, as it were in an ecstasy, addressed him:

"Power! Power, my friend! Nothing like it. Luxury is nothing, my friend. Power is everything. The power is not in the machinery. It's in ourselves. It's in me, me! Without me, the machinery would stop. By the way, I'm the new chairman of the–"

He ceased, staring in alarm across the huge hall.

Julia had come in, and was approaching him, upheld by the arm of Forfar.

"Damn that fellow!" Flitfoot breathed to himself. "He had the infernal insolence to be in love with her. And now he's–"

"Baby is dead!" cried Julia, panting and terribly distraught. "It's London has killed her. But you would have it."

Her eyes blazed at him.

His face was yellow. He sank to the floor in a heap. The others bent over his form. Julia clutched him passionately.

He murmured feebly:

"Sligo! Sligo! I want to dictate some letters."

The next moment he was dead.

"The aneurism!" breathed Forfar. "Bound to finish him in the end!"

The machinery continued to revolve as though nothing had happened. Flitfoot was carried away. The hall was empty save for the machinery, which went on exactly as usual.

CHAPTER XL

At the double funeral, which was attended by Julia and Sir Joshua, and by the members of the electrical staffs and of Flitfoot's own staff, as the procession was moving towards the graveside, a decrepit and shabby old man mysteriously joined it, – Chail.

Julia was interested in him.

"Who are you?" she enquired sadly.

"I'm nobody of any importance," said Chail.

"Did you know my poor husband?"

"Yes, madam," Chail answered. "He was very kind to me.

PART III

THE CINEMATIC CONCLUSION

Return to the Punch and Judy show.

The show is finished. The audience disperses. The Punch and Judy man shuts up his collapsible sentry-box. He throws his wooden marionettes negligently into the chest, and stamps carelessly on the lid because it won't close properly. With the aid of his wife, and followed by his dog, he wheels the entire concern away in search of new audiences.

Then is seen a large vision of tens, scores, hundreds of Punch and Judy shows, confused, running into one another, vibrating, incomprehensible. And the Punch and Judy man again, trundling his tent away. Life!

EXPLANATORY NOTES

PART I, THE FILM SCENARIO

1. *the usual Punch and Judy show*: Bennett's version of *Punch and Judy* adheres in the main to the basic format of the traditional puppet show which made its first recorded appearance in England in 1662. The story in its present form is attributed to an early 17th century Italian comedian, Silvio Fiorello. Samuel Pepys records seeing a marionette *Punch and Judy* show in Covent Garden, performed by an Italian puppeteer, Pietro Gimonde. Marionette shows featuring Punch were at their height in the early 1700s, becoming extremely popular in Paris and the American colonies later in the century. Marionette shows were, however, expensive to mount and cumbersome to transport and by the end of the eighteenth century had begun to give way to glove puppet shows.

By Victorian times *Punch and Judy* shows were performed from within a narrow lightweight booth by a single puppeteer. Known as 'Professor' he might have an assistant, or 'bottler', to whip up enthusiasm in the audience and to collect money. Today the show remains an integral part of traditional British seaside culture, with regular summer seasons at resorts such as Weston-super-Mare and Llandudno.

There is no single definitive version of *Punch and Judy.* The first known printed script is by John Payne Collier, with illustrations by George Cruickshank, published in 1828. Henry Mayhew's *London Labour and the London Poor* (1851) includes an interview with a Punch and Judy puppeteer, together with a full transcript of a typical 1840's performance. But Punch remains primarily an oral tradition and performers improvise around well-established short scenes depicting interaction between two characters. Punch, in a fit of jealousy, strangles his infant child, and kills his wife when she attacks him in retaliation. He goes on to triumph over Ennui, in the shape of the dog Toby, Disease, in the shape of the doctor, and even over Death itself. Bennett's Punch fails this final test of strength.

The illustrated weekly satirical magazine *Punch, or The London Chariva*, was founded in 1840 and until 1969 the figures of Punch and Toby usually appeared somewhere on the front cover. Cruickshank, Mayhew, and William Thackeray were all associated with the periodical at some time.

2. *the latest book describing the* 'Punch and Judy' *performance:* I have been

unable to trace the specific book to which Bennett refers. There were several books about Punch and Judy published during the 1920s, including Mary Stewart's *The Land of Punch and Judy: A Book of Puppet Plays for Children* (1922) and Maurice Baring's *Punch and Judy and Other Essays* (1924).

3. *Scaramouch*: a character from the *Italian commedia*, usually portrayed as a buffoon or a boastful clown. He became one of the iconic Punch and Judy puppets and is sometimes shown as owning a dog. He is frequently the object of violent blows to the head from Punch, causing his head to fall off his shoulders. It is this latter characteristic that accounts for the term Scaramouch being applied to a class of puppets with extendable necks.

4. *the Negro:* when he revised his film scenario (Part I) Bennett crossed through his typed references to the Negro puppet in sections 7 and 8. In so doing he was reflecting the gradual disappearance of the character from performances in the twentieth century.

PART II, THE NOVEL

Chapter I

1. *a chow:* known in China for over two thousand years, the first recorded appearance of the Chow in England was in 1789. Organised breeding began in 1887 and the breed was recognised by the Kennel Club in 1894. They began to be shown in the 1920s and a number appeared at Crufts in 1925. At the time of Bennett's story they were extremely popular with the rich and famous - U.S.A. President Calvin Coolidge owned a red and a black Chow, and Sigmund Freud was reportedly a fan of the breed. The Chow is a powerfully built dog with a mane that gives it the appearance of a miniature lion. Had it been available to him at the time, Flitfoot might have benefited from reading *The Reader's Digest Illustrated Book of Dogs* (1984): 'It does not take easily to strangers and is sometimes unfriendly or aggressive towards them' (p.110).

2. *Tidal Power Shares*: a young American engineer, Dexter P. Cooper, first proposed a tidal power plan for Washington County. There were plans in hand to raise a million dollars from private capital to fund construction but the stock market crash of 1929 put an end to private investment at the same time as removing public support. There were also plans for tidal energy plants in France in the 1920s but these early attempts were abandoned for lack of funds.

3. *the Buff book:* these were detailed reference books for the various districts of London similar to the modern telephone directory. *Hansard*'s record of Parliamentary debate for 30 November 1920 shows the Paymaster-General being asked whether the Buff book would be forwarded to all telephone subscribers as a matter of course.

Chapter IV

1. *Amen Corner:* Miss Sligo's Bagdad Café was probably set at the junction of Paternoster Row and Ave Maria Lane, just to the west of St. Paul's Cathedral, in the City of London.

Chapter V

1. *Electricity supply*: London's electricity was supplied by a number of private companies, some of which were comparatively small and that were dedicated to supplying a single industry or group of factories. There were, at the time Bennett was writing, two large and growing companies - the London Power Company, supplying West London, and the County of London Electric Supply Company, supplying the East.

2. *Somerset House:* located on the south side of the Strand in central London, it housed the Inland Revenue after its creation by a merger of the Stamp and Taxes Offices and the Excise Department in 1849.

Chapter VIII

1. *the Grand Babylon Hotel*: Bennett's novel *The Grand Babylon Hotel* was published in 1902 after serialisation in the *Golden Penny* magazine. Bennett features the hotel in many of his novels and stories.

2. *the Government will be forced by public opinion to buy out all your private electricity companies:* a chaotic system in which there was a variety of standards of frequency and voltage across London led to Parliament deciding in 1925 that a unified system under public ownership was desirable, although in the event it took another 30 years for the electricity supply to be nationalised.

3. *Power-stations one after another*: in the 1920s several companies merged to form the London Power Company which then planned a number of large power-stations for London. The first of these was in the Battersea area.

Chapter IX

1. *The Majestic:* when Denry Machin travels to London in Chapter III of *The Regent* (1913) he initially planned to stay at the Majestic Hotel, a cheaper but acceptable alternative to the Grand Babylon Hotel.

Chapter X

1. *Bovril:* John Lawson Johnston developed a thick salty meat extract drink in the 1870s which was trademarked as Bovril in 1886. By the early 1900s hot cups of Bovril were so popular that their merits were advertised by an electric advertising sign in Piccadilly Circus. Later owned by Unilever, it was made in Burton upon Trent, Staffordshire.

2. *Whitechapel and Aldgate:* an inner-city district of the London borough of Tower Hamlets, Whitechapel gained notoriety as the site of the Jack the Ripper murders in the late 1880s. From the 1840s onward, along with Aldgate and other East end areas, it had become a warren of insanitary small dark enclaves and was still a very poor area at the time of Bennett's writing in 1928.

3. *doing him in in the back with a pair of scissors:* the symbolism of scissors linked to sex, madness and death occurs in Bennett's novel *The Old Wives' Tale* (1908). The former shop assistant Maria Critchlow finds something deeply disturbing about her late middle-age marriage and attempts suicide by stabbing herself with a pair of scissors after wildly confessing to deranged flashbacks of 'sexual irregularity with her late employer, Samuel Povey' (p.530). (For a more detailed discussion of the symbolic sexual significance of scissors, see the 'Introduction' to the Churnet Valley Books Centenary Edition of *The Old Wives' Tale*.)

4. *Ealing:* a suburban area of West London some 12 miles from the City of London.

Chapter XI

1. *St. James's Street:* is one of London's principle central streets, running from Piccadilly to St. James's Palace and Pall Mall. It boasts several of the capital's best-known gentlemen's clubs, exclusive shops and a variety of offices.

Chapter XII

1. *You'd better go and see a picture:* in effect Sir Joshua is excluding his daughter from the perceived masculine sphere of financial decision making and literally and metaphorically banishing her to the silent sphere of cinema. Interestingly, female critics such as Dorothy Richardson were writing about cinema's increasingly large female audience and beginning to theorise silent cinema as a space empowering women's voices in the most direct way as they insisted on talking through silent films, discussing either screen events or their own domestic affairs. Richardson writes:

> The conversation may be more interesting than the film.... For all her bad manners that will doubtless be pruned when the film becomes high art and its temple a temple of stillness save for the music that at present inspires her to do her worst, she is innocently, directly, albeit unconsciously, upon the path that men have reached through long centuries of effort and thought.

('Continuous Performance VIII', 1928,
Reprinted in *Close Up 1927-1933 Cinema and Modernism*, pp. 174-176)

Chapter XVI

1. *The Big Five banks:* in the immediate post-World War I period the so-called 'Big Five' clearing banks Barclays Bank, Midland Bank (now part of HSBC), Lloyds (now merged to form Lloyds TSB as part of the Lloyds Banking Group), National Westminster (now part of the Royal Bank of Scotland Group and referred to as NatWest), National Provincial Bank (merged with the National Westminster in 1970) - formed a cartel in the banking industry. Lucy Newton writes: 'The amalgamation movement resulted in centralisation, bureaucratisation and formalisation in banking, as opposed to the "relationship" banking that was previously predominant' (*Branding, marketing and product innovation: the attempts of British banks to reach consumers in the inter-war period.* www.henley.reading.ac.uk; 2008). At the same time as this consolidation was taking place there was a corresponding reduction in the degree of personal ties and trust that had previously existed between banks and their customers.

Chapter XVII

1. *The following scene might perhaps run in and out simultaneously with the previous scene*: Bennett's technical suggestion refers to the editing practice

of crosscutting in a narrational process by means of which two or more lines of action taking place in different locations are woven together. Within each separate sequence the events occur consecutively, but between the lines of action taken as wholes the temporal relations are simultaneous. In the 1930s crosscutting became far less frequent because of the technical problems involved in quickly cutting from one line of dialogue to another in sound film. David Bordwell, Janet Staiger and Kristen Thompson in *The Classical Hollywood Cinema. Film Style & Mode of Production to 1960* (London: Routledge, 1988), include a brief history of crosscutting in which they construct a line of continuity with narrational point-of-view in literature and nineteenth century drama, and trace W. G. Griffith's parallel montage - in *Birth of a Nation* (1915) and *Intolerance* (1916) - back through theatrical melodrama to Dickens's novels. For a comprehensive discussion of crosscutting as a filmic narrational technique see David Bordwell's *Narration in the Fiction Film.*

2. *John C. Curtiss's triumph*: in drawing attention to Curtiss's success in the art auction, Bennett is extending the behavioural traits he shares with the real-life character upon whom he is in part based, the American financier Charles Yerkes (see Note 3 below). Yerkes amassed an impressive collection of French paintings. Following the 1893 Chicago World Fair's inclusion of Auguste Rodin's work, Yerkes acquired two of his marbles, *Orpheus,* and *Cupid and Psyche,* the first of Rodin's works to have gone to an American collector.

3. *Yerkes:* Charles Tyson Yerkes (1837-1905) was an American financier who played a leading role in developing public transport systems in Chicago and London. He opened his own brokerage firm and joined the Philadelphia stock exchange in 1859 at the age of 22. Six years later he had moved into banking and became the financial agent for the City of Philadelphia's treasurer, using public money in stock speculations. When the Great Chicago fire of 1871 caused a financial panic, his dealings were exposed and led to a term of imprisonment.

Released from prison after just seven months, amongst rumours of blackmail involving leading local politicians, Yerkes spent the next ten years rebuilding his lost fortune. In 1882 he moved to Chicago where he eventually came to control a large section of the City's tramway and railway systems, through a series of astute and convoluted business deals. His ruthless business methods, however, brought him once again into disrepute and he was forced to relocate to New York.

Yerkes arrived in New York having sold the majority of his Chicago transport stocks, and with his considerable fortune of $15 million intact. Here he was approached to help finance the electrification of London's District Railway. Moving to London in 1900 he went on to establish the Underground Electric Railways Company, took control of the Metropolitan District Railway and acquired interests in the partially constructed Baker Street & Waterloo Railway. Wishing to also control the Piccadilly line, Yerkes resorted to his ruthless dealing skills to out-manoeuvre his fellow American industrialist, J.P. Morgan, and prevent him from entering the London Underground field.

Yerkes died from kidney failure back in New York, aged 68, in 1905, his financial affairs once again in disarray.

4. *that fellow H. G. Wells:* Bennett and Wells were great friends, corresponding regularly from September 1897 until a few weeks before Bennett's death in March 1931. Between June 1895 and September 1930 Bennett wrote no less than 52 articles discussing Wells's work and reviewing his books.

Chapter XXV

1. *the special aeroplane landed at Croydon:* two small adjacent Royal Flying Corps airfields were set up in Croydon in 1915 as part of a defensive strategy aimed at combating German Zeppelin raids over London. They combined in 1920 to become part of Croydon Aerodrome, London's first official airport for all international flights to and from the capital. It was also the first airport in the world to introduce air traffic control technology.

Chapter XXVI1

1. *'You ought to be x-rayed':* the German physicist Wilhelm Roentgen discovered the penetrative properties of x-rays in November 1895 when he was able to take an image of his wife's hand. Hospitals began acquiring x-ray equipment the following year. During World War I x-ray equipment became a standard component of field hospitals. The Society of Radiographers was formed in 1920. The absence of protection around the early x-ray tubes resulted in a considerable number of injuries to the operators, which led to the setting up of the British X-ray and Radium Protection Committee.

2. *a place in Welbeck Street*: London's Welbeck Hospital is at 27 Welbeck Street. It was established in the early 1920s.

Chapter XXXVII

1. *All the furniture in the room was of the Queen Anne period*: the style of furniture in fashion during the reign of Queen Anne (1702-1714) was notably smaller, lighter and generally more comfortable than that of its immediate predecessors. It is often referred to as late Baroque.

Chapter XXXVIII

1. *a semi-detached villa in Golder's Green*: an area in the London Borough of Barnet. Essentially a nineteenth century suburban commuting development, it is some 5 1/2 miles north west of Charing Cross.

APPENDIX I

THE FILM 'STORY'

(*CLOSE UP*, DECEMBER 1927)

One can only judge by one's own experience. My own experience is limited. I have not spent every evening of the last twenty years in film-theatres. But, so far as my limited experience enables me to judge, I consider that America has no artistic importance whatever in the world of the cinema. Technically, in the matter of camera-craft, it has had importance. Commercially it has had, and still has, great importance. The financial methods, the absurd extravagance, the indifference to economic principles which have characterised film-exploitation in America would have ruined any industry with less rich opportunities and less vast fields of activity than the films. One hears rumours of the perilous position of some of the big companies. The marvel is that they have not all gone bankrupt.

As regards the artistic future of the film, it would not matter – provided that Chaplin were saved – if all Hollywood were swallowed up in an earthquake. The loss of life would be terrible and deplorable; the domestic tragedies would be agonizing; tens of millions of simple souls would sincerely mourn in five continents; but the artistic future of the film world would not suffer in the slightest degree. I have never – Chaplin's work apart – seen a good American film. I have rarely seen one that was not artistically revolting. Not one of the famous American directors has left a permanent mark on film history, or produced anything that would not deeply grieve the judicious.

I must specially except Charles Chaplin, who, in addition

to being a great actor, is a great producer. *The Gold Rush,* while not perfect in some essential matters, was a great film. It would bear seeing twice.

The future of the films seems to me to be in Germany. I have seen dreadful German films. One of the silliest and worst was *Metropolis*. But I have seen two relatively good ones, *The Last Laugh*, and, still better, *Vaudeville*. *The Last Laugh* was too long, too confused, and too sentimental in the middle; but towards the end the director pulled himself together and created real effective comedy which was conceived with a true appreciation of the medium. The photography frequently had beauty.

Vaudeville told a convincing story, spoilt only by lack of attention to detail. Surely it must have been obvious to even the common intelligence that no gymnasts engaged in dangerous acrobatic feats every evening could possibly have indulged in the nocturnal excesses which the strong men of *Vaudeville* permitted themselves. The photography was beautiful. By which I mean that the pictorial composition, both statically and dynamically, was beautiful. The eye was again and again charmed by beautiful pictures made out of men and women and out of common interiors. To achieve this was a feat.

And I have seen finer compositional results than those of *Vaudeville*. A few weeks ago, in Berlin, a small party of which I happened to be a member was given a private performance of a film (I will not name it, as it is not yet released) whose photography in my opinion reached a higher level than any film has ever reached before. It was an almost continuous series of lovely pictures. The beauty of them thrilled us. And the acting was fairly good. But the story told by the lovely pictures was contemptible. It had no intelligible basic idea, nor any convincingness, nor any characterisation, nor any beauty. The plot was involved, obscure, and slow in movement. And the invention of illustrative incident was puerile. Indeed the story was merely foolish.

I mention this film because it suddenly crystallised my critical notions about the present state of development of the cinema. It constituted a superlative illustration of the fact that while the graphic side of the cinema has been most satisfactorily advancing, the dramatic side has been most unsatisfactorily lagging behind. The creative brain which conceived and executed the graphic side in a manner to win the respect of the artistically educated seemed to possess no critical faculty capable of handling the dramatic side in a way correspondingly adequate.

Apparently the leaders of the cinema have not yet grasped the fundamental truth that the most important part of any creative film is the story itself, and that all other parts of the enterprise are merely parts of an effort to tell the story.

In other words they forget, or they disdain, the central reason for their work. They are so excited and so busy in "producing" that they lose sight of what it is they *are* producing. The act of creation interests them far less that the act of "putting over" that which has been created. In the judgment of the master-brain of the affair, the author is subordinate to the interpreter. The master-brain thinks first of how much he can spend on the business, not of how little. Instead of trying first to derive strength *from* the main theme, the master-brain tries first to give strength *to* the theme. The master-brain is occupied with extraneous ornament instead of being occupied with dramatic essentials.

Any story will serve for a star-producer. And if by chance he gets hold of a good story he is sure somehow to ruin it by preposterous additions. I have not yet seen a first-rate story told in a first-rate style on the screen. All the new stories, contrived *ad hoc*, are conventional, grossly sentimental, clumsy, and fatally impaired by poverty of invention. The screen has laid hands on some of the greatest stories in the world, and has cheapened, soiled, ravaged, and poisoned them by the crudest fatuities.

Even Charles Chaplin shows immensely less talent for devising a tale, than for any of the subsidiary branches of film-work.

It is no answer here to say that the big public demands bad stories. The big public may or may not demand bad stories. I am discussing, not the commercial aspect of the screen, but the question of its artistic progress. I am thinking of art and not of dividends. Those who think first of vast expense and vaster returns will never do anything for the film as an artistic vehicle. In regard to finance I will only say this – that it costs less to do an artistic film than an inartistic film. Chariot-races, the dividing of seas for the passage of hosts, conflagrations, battles on water and battles on land may make an audience stare, but what grips and moves an audience is the simple spectacle of human emotions clashing one with another.

The remedy is clear. If and when a producer acquires the true sense of proposition which alone will enable him to perceive the relative importance of the different parts of his job, he must, unless he has himself the gift of creating character and contriving event, find somebody who has that gift – in terms of the screen. Useless for him to go to established and therefore middle-aged masters of literary narration. To all these distinguished artists the screen is still a novelty. The film-medium does not come naturally to them because they were not familiar with it in their formative years – the only years that count in the making of an artist. The producer must discover young men who went to the cinema as children, who cannot remember the time when there was no cinema, and who will take to the screen as a duck takes to water. The older men who accept an invitation to the screen are bound to resemble ducks endeavouring to fly. They may fly, but their flight will be laborious, maladroit and pathetic.

All which is obvious; the obvious, however, is often useful.

APPENDIX II

ARNOLD BENNETT:

JOURNAL 1929 (pp. 45-47)

Dinner and interview with a star film-director. I was told that he was the finest and the most successful film-director in the country. I had never seen anything of his on the screen. A youngish man, with a clear, penetrating voice, trained no doubt to make itself heard in the immensities of studios, but more than adequate for a dinner-table. I had written and sold a film scenario, and at the request of the purchasing firm the director was considering the same.

At first he assumed the air of a puissant law-giver. When resolutely tackled, however, he changed the air for another one, and we became almost equals. He argued on the following lines: "Now the hero of your story is a financier. Now would a street-barrow woman in Hoxton understand about getting an overdraft at a Bank? That is the test, the street-barrow woman in Hoxton. Is office work and typewriting romantic? *Is it*? Now if we could have the story lowered in class, if for instance you could make the financier a ring-master in a circus, now that would be colourful. What we want is colour." And so on in similar style.

I argued him out of every point, and soon his principal phrase was, "Oh! I agree." But though he agreed point by point, he did not agree in the least on the whole question. I yielded on nothing. He yielded on everything, and said at last he would think the matter over. But I was quite certain that he never would think it over.

The purchasing firm had specially commissioned me to write a story that did not resemble the ordinary film-story. They knew my more notorious books, and desired a story in the manner and on the plane of those books. I had asked them if they wanted truth to life, and they had replied that truth to life was precisely what they did want and that on the screen truth to life was coming more and more into fashion! Audiences were getting tired of sobstuff, etc. I now perceived that, if audiences were getting tired of sobstuff, film-directors were not. Film-directors still had their eye on the purely imaginary woman in Hoxton. The purchasing firm had reckoned without their film-directors, and film-directors had the last word.

This particular film-director could choose between film-stories. He was very far from being a fool. Intelligent in his own way; but it was a crude way. There was certainly something of the artist in him. Some creative fire in him. I liked him.

When we had thrashed the story all to bits and neither he nor I had anything more to say about it, he grew communicative about himself, in reply to my questions, and revealed himself a regular figure out of film-land. He said: "I can never begin work until about eleven-thirty in the morning. I have a glass of sherry then, and that starts the flow of ideas. You must have the flow. The film must move rapidly, and so your ideas must come rapidly." An odd argument, but I don't think he could see any flaw in it.

I found that in order to impress him I had to boast. Hence I did boast. I called down rather sharply one of the head-waiters who had been too curt with me. This episode obviously increased the director's respect for me. When the interview was over he said he should not require his car, and amiably offered to send me home in it. It was a magnificent, a glorious car, the car of the legendary film-director. I thanked him and said that I might just as well go home in my own.

This book is one of a series of Arnold Bennett titles, published both as an attractive and uniform paperback and as a limited and numbered hardback edition:

HELEN WITH THE HIGH HAND

LEONORA

THE REGENT

THE PRICE OF LOVE

A MAN FROM THE NORTH

THE OLD WIVES' TALE

THE PRETTY LADY

THE CARD

ARNOLD BENNETT'S UNCOLLECTED SHORT STORIES

LORD DOVER & OTHER LOST STORIES

The Card is Arnold Bennett's most popular novel and its hero, Denry Machin, has become one of fiction's most memorable characters.

Denry's story has universal appeal. It tells of the unlikely rise of its hero from a poor working class single parent family to become the admired and loved Mayor of Bursley. Denry's cheeky chappy exploits are often questionable but his motives are always well-intentioned.

Whether it is looking to celebrities for business endorsements, escaping disastrous romantic entanglements or saving the local football team, Denry inhabits a world that remains instantly recognisable today. Yet beneath all Bennett's sophisticated slapstick comedy there runs a deep vein of social commentary.

This Centenary edition reproduces the original text. It is also lavishly illustrated with scenes from the famous 1952 film starring Alec Guinness, Glynis Johns and Petula Clark.

Uncollected Short Stories 1892-1932

From the Potteries to Penzance

Edited and

Published together for the first time, these stories are a valuable and entertaining addition to the Arnold Bennett canon. They offer a treasure house of gems taken from the Golden Age of magazine short stories.

Spanning forty years from late-Victorian Britain to the 1930s Depression, they take us on a journey from London to the Potteries and to the far South West. As we travel we read of lost love, ghostly mysteries, terrorist plots, murder, marital discord, war-time profiteering, social high-jinks, romance - the whole range of life as seen through the eyes of a master craftsman.

The inclusion of many of the original magazine illustrations provides an additional pleasure.

The Introduction and Notes help to place Bennett's stories in the context of British literary, social and political life of the time, opening up a wealth of new material for further exploration by scholars. Above all else, they add to "the great cause of cheering us all up".

"I am delighted to see my Grandfather's stories so lovingly restored. This is also an important work of scholarship."
Denis Eldin, President of the Arnold Bennett Society.

Cover by Sally Richardson

198 x 129 mm Paperback 448 pages
ISBN 9781904546740 *£9.95*

210 x 148 mm Hardback, 200 limited edition £16.95

Edited and

Cover by Sally Richardson

198 x 129 mm Paperback 288 pages

ISBN 9781904546818 *£9.95*

210 x 148 mm Hardback, limited to 200 £14.95

198 x 129 mm Paperback 384 pages
ISBN 1904546689 *£9.95*

210 x 148 mm Hardback, numbered, £14.95